To Kate &

keep fus

Jess Miller

Nicest pair of "Jobee Jabbing Tea leafs" I have ever met!!...

Lovely to meet you both.... Can't believe I lost out on the coins game, but Chris you did us proud

Yours Neil Skimgeour xxx

This book is dedicated to the late, great, highland ghillie, my very good friend:

Jimmy McLean

Who I write about in this book.

My sincere thanks to those who took me fishing, taught me to fish and fished with me down the years, it was my great privilege to have known you.

To the wondrous life form that is the Atlantic salmon for teaching me patience, perseverance, humility, appreciation, much about myself and life and most of all - how to fish for you!

Thanks to Paul Zissler, John & Lavender Buckland, Ross Gardiner, Kathryn Marcellino, Lyn Davies, Liz Tomkins, Rupert Suren, Rex Sumner, Martin Docherty and everyone who supports me in so many ways.

Donations from the proceeds of this book will be made to Conservation Organisations working in countries that enjoy the presence of Atlantic Salmon to conserve these spectacular fish and their habitat for those who come after.

Jess Miller's

True or False Fishing Stories 1

A semi-autobiographical account of fishing happenings and humour!

The full Prize List, can be found at: TrueorFalseFishingStories.com

MY BEST ADVICE

Read through the Glossary of Terms
before commencing the stories!

That is unless you consider yourself an expert.
Definition of an expert:
'X' is the unknown quantity, 'spurt' is a drip under pressure....

www.TrueorFalseFishingStories.com

Available in print, download and audiobook formats somewhere out there!

Jess Miller's 100 True or False Fishing Stories! (free entry competition)

© MillerBooks 2012 ISBN: 978-0-9572482-8-1 First published in 2013 by MillerBooks www.TrueorFalseFishingStories.com

100 short stories & anecdotes from Jess's fishing life in the UK, especially on Scotland's river Tay fishing for Atlantic Salmon. 10 stories are not true, but even some of the true ones are pretty unbelievable! Enter the free competition at: www.TrueorFalseFishingStories.com

Cover: Jess & Kathryn Marcellino www.MarcellinoDesign.com

Cover Cartoon: Lyn Davies www.lyndavies.utopicstudios.com © Jess Miler & MillerBooks 2013

Interior Illustrations: Liz Tomkins www.ArtinBrittany.com © Jess Miller & MillerBooks 2013

Jess's other titles:

Jess Miller's 120 True or False Fishing Stories! **To be published 30th April 2014!**
With a new free entry competition

120 stories from Jess's fishing experiences in the UK, Madeira, Norway, Sweden, USA, British Columbia, Russia, Siberia. Out of these riotous, hilarious, fascinating and downright stupid stories 10 are not true! Free competition entries will be at: www.TrueorFalseFishingStories.com

The Great Convergence
© 2000 Jester Publications & 2010 MillerBooks ISBN: 978-0-9565831-3-0 www.EnergyThieves.com

A light-hearted, humorous tale recounting the strange encounters and even stranger goings on, the scheming, greed, deceit, hilarity, chaos and triumph that occur when thousands of people unexpectedly converge upon a simple English village auction. (Includes some fishing!)

We're All In This Together - Help Through Stressful and Depressive Times
© 2000 Jester Publications & 2010 MillerBooks ISBN: 978-0-9565831-2-3 www.EnergyThieves.com

Explaining the journey we travel down into and back from depression and giving twelve simple, but powerful, proven self-help therapies that anyone can use to make themselves feel better in stressful or depressive times. In a large font and well spaced for those who are in difficulty.

How to Beat the Energy Thieves® And Make Your Life Better - Book 1
Alcohol, Drugs, Tobacco, Bullying, Stealing, Gambling, Gangs, Knives, Guns
© MillerBooks 2010 First published in 2010 by MillerBooks ISBN: 978-0-9565831-0-9 www.EnergyThieves.com

If you don't understand you have been created as energy then you can't work out how to protect your energy against everything that will try to steal it from you in order to divert you from your true path and make your life hurt. In this ground breaking self-help book Jess Miller gives you clear, concise ways to deal with the energy thieves that are damaging your energy so you can forge your way down the road of good and guide yourself to a better life.

How to Beat the Energy Thieves® And Make Your Life Better - Book 2
Emotions, Food, People, Major Problems, Traumas, How to Win
© MillerBooks 2010 ISBN: 978-0-9565831-1-6 First published in 2010 by MillerBooks www.EnergyThieves.com

How to stop emotions such as fear, loneliness, anger or hatred holding your energy hostage.
How to resist turning food into an energy thief.
How to get the better of people who are acting as energy thieves against you.
How to beat exam or public speaking nerves.
How to cope with financial wipe-out.
How to beat the energy thieves that live in your past and hurt you in the present.
Unique and powerful insights to help you protect your energy and find your way to a better life.

Book 3 will be published in 2014

How to Beat the Energy Thieves®And Make Your Life Better - Book 3
Education, Indoctrination, The Media, Technology, Role Models, Gossip, Trivia, Bigotry, Hypocrisy, Self Importance, Narcissism, Arrogance, Judgementalism
© MillerBooks 2010 To be published in 2013 by MillerBooks ISBN: 978-0-9565831-4-7 www.EnergyThieves.com

How your life teachers may not be teaching you the best way to live out your existence.
How your training by the system we live under enables it to control your energy.
How the media influences your understanding about life and the way you live it.
How technology can be an energy thief unless you use it only for what you absolutely need.
How role models can have a dramatic affect on the direction your life takes.
How idle gossip can ruin your life and the lives of others.
How the trivia of life can consistently bog down your energy.
How self importance and arrogance can steal your energy.
How judging yourself is always better than standing in judgement of others.

Competition Prizes:

A selection of our competition prizes are advertised at the beginning of the book.

The full, ever increasing Prize List can be found at:

TrueorFalseFishingStories.com

Gordonian Fishings

Newtyle Beat, River Tay, Dunkeld, Perthshire

Fishing prize sponsor of these options:

4 days for 2 rods in spring
or 6 days for 2 rods in June/July
or 3 days for 2 rods in September/October

Includes ghillie and boat/bank rotation

Newtyle returned 180 fish during the 2012 season

The beat provides fish all year round and offers good fly water
It flows through the stunning scenery of the highland fault

For information and bookings: newtylefishings@gmail.com

www.GordonianFishings.co.uk

Dunkeld House Fishings

River Tay, Dunkeld, Perthshire

Fishing prize sponsor of:

1 day for 2 rods with boat & ghillie
1 day for 2 rods bank fishing

Dunkeld House beat is 1¾ miles averaging 150 fish
This is the main water Jess writes about in this book

Hilton Dunkeld House stands on the banks of this beat

For information and bookings:

Simon Furniss Mobile: +44 (0)7736 379104

https://www.facebook.com/DunkeldHouseFishings

Foreword:

For the first four and a half decades of my life I lived and breathed fishing for one of nature's most glorious life forms - the Atlantic Salmon.

In 1968 we moved to Dunkeld House Hotel on the banks of Scotland's largest salmon river, the Tay, where I had been fishing since I was a boy.

Salmon fishing taught me a lot about life and myself, helped me recover from a life threatening illness and kept me sane whilst an angry young man.

I was unbelievably lucky to experience the vast runs of Tay spring salmon that have people labelling me a crazy person when I talk about them these days, because the spring runs are sadly so depleted.

For me it's like looking back at a previous life because nowadays I spend my time writing self help books and helping people beat their life problems at EnergyThieves.com.

A friend recently observed that I've lived at least seven lives this lifetime that he knows of and, as luck would have it, I had written down much of what happened during my fishing life for my auto biography, which I hope to publish in 2015......... maybe!

But as my clock of life is ticking I decided to publish 100 fishing stories here as a semi-autobiographical record of my fishing life for you to enjoy.

90 of them are true, 10 are not. Can you guess which ones?

If you would like a chance to win one of many great prizes to be announced throughout the competition which ends on 30th April 2014 please register at: TrueorFalseFishingStories.com and enter the numbers of the ten stories you think are not true - for free!

Please send me your true or false fishing or shooting/hunting stories through the website for inclusion in future books.

And have fun working out which 10 stories are not true.

After all, having fun is what fishing, and life, should be all about!

Jess Miller

Glossary of Terms

Backing - Line put on a fly reel before the fly line to increase its capacity.

Bass – A salmon bass is a bag for carrying salmon.

Beat – A stretch of river owned by someone just as you would own a house. In Scotland the owner of a beat is called a 'riparian owner'.
Only the Scots know what 'riparian' means and they won't tell anyone.

A blank week – A week when nothing is caught.

A blank expression – On your face at the end of a blank week.

Blethering – Scottish word for talking for ages about nothing in particular. When doing so you can be labelled 'a blether'.

Boorach – Scottish word meaning getting your fishing line in a bad tangle, something like a 'fankle'.

Carrion – Stuff a Hoody Crow feeds on.

Central Belt – The area of Scotland encompassing Glasgow and Edinburgh, etc.

Char - Or Charr, an Arctic fish that can be found in many Scottish lochs.

Clutch – A clicking drag system on a fishing reel for putting pressure on a fish. Not a group of eggs that a bird, such as a duck, sits on to hatch.

Cobblers – Colloquial British slang word used when ridiculing someone or being dismissive. Polite slang for testicles.

The Crack – Talking, blethering, usually with some hilarity.

Croy – A construction of stones extending out into a river, either completely or part under the water. Fish will run up either side of the stream created below a croy and rest above it. Sometimes called a 'groin', which I have never understood.

Dram – A large whisky.

Large Dram – An even larger whisky.

Bloody Large Dram – You decide.....I can't remember.

Drogue - An underwater 'parachute' that stops boats drifting too fast in high wind.

Devon Minnow – A salmon lure with two small 'wings' that make it spin. Devons are usually painted two colours along their length, one on top and one below, but can also be one single colour. They can be all sizes from tiny to 4 inches or more, can be made of metal, wood or both or quill or plastic and they have a single treble hook at the tail end. Often referred to as a 'spinner'.

Dour – When referring to a person this is a Scottish word that means they are no fun. Can also refer to the state of the weather.

Downstream – If you look 'down' a river, with the water flowing away from you, you are looking downstream.

Dropper – A short piece of nylon to which is tied a fly to be fished from a fly cast, or to a weight to be fished from a swivel. Normally fished a foot or two up the line from whatever bait is being fished on the end. A proper 'Loch Leven' fly cast has three droppers, with three flies tied to them, and a tail fly. Which makes, er, four.

Duck – Something a cricket batsman can be dismissed for – zero, nada, zilch, nothing. Should not be confused with:

Duck – A duck.

Factor – In Scotland a man who is in charge of an estate (land and property) on behalf of the estate owner.
The owner invariably thinks the factor is in charge and doing a good job.
Some factors are not only not in charge, but are not doing a good job either.
Should not be confused with:

Factor – Something that can affect something else and that consequently ought to be taken into account.
Completely different from the previous 'factor' anyway.

Fankle – Scottish word meaning getting your fishing line in a bad tangle, something like a 'boorach'.

Ferox - Large Brown Trout that feeds on smaller fish.

Fish – Atlantic Salmon. In Scotland they are referred to only as 'a fish' or 'fish' as it is considered there is no other fish worthy of such title.

Fu' – Scottish word meaning drunk (*full*).

Gaff – A large steel hook used for hooking salmon out of the river in days gone by. I carried a Hardy telescopic gaff for emergency situations on high banks and self defence purposes against poachers for many years.

Gannet – A large sea bird with a voracious appetite, unwittingly mimicked by a large number of human beings.

Ghillie – Often incorrectly written as 'gillie', but the Scottish spelling of the word is indeed 'ghillie'. A Scottish gamekeeper who takes you fishing on river or loch.

Grayling – Fish introduced to the river Tay by Monks in days gone by. They were prolific (the Grayling not the Monks) until their numbers, along with those of the Tay's native wild brown trout, were slaughtered during the 1970's, mainly by Scotland's central belt 'trout fishers'.

Grilse – A young salmon returning to the river for the first time. The main grilse run comes in the summer and they vary in size from one to sixteen pounds or more. Normal size is under ten pounds.
Same word for singular or plural, however Americans for some reason tend to talk about them as Gril, both singular and plural.

Guy Dreach – Not a person, but a Scottish description of miserable weather.

Harling – A form of fishing where the boat is kept steady in the river by use of an outboard engine manned by a ghillie whilst two or three rods are fished from the stern with their lures fishing in the current some distance behind the boat. In the old days ghillies used to row all day long, but not today. The river is traversed and slowly fished downstream ensuring that every salmon lie is covered.

Head-and-Tailer – Used to describe fish as they roll just under the surface whilst running a river. You only see their head, the top of their back and tail. Sometimes you see them doing this as they chop across the top of a specific stream or current.
So why aren't they called 'Head-Top-of-the-Back-and-Tailers'?
Don't be a pratt.

Hoodie Crow – A type of crow that feeds on carrion.

Jack Pike – A young pike. We used to have a guest at our hotel called Jack Snipe (who was actually not a small bird, but a real person).

Keeper – Gamekeeper who manages ground and organises hunts for game animals and birds, like a guide in North America.

Kelt – A spent salmon that has spawned and is attempting to get back to the sea. Most don't make it, but those that do may return as really big fish if all the things that kill them in the sea (such as human beings) are unsuccessful.
It is illegal in Scotland to kill a kelt.

Kidology – The art of kidding someone.

Kynoch Killer - A 'plug' type of lure shaped like an ice cream cone with an oblique scoop out of the thick end. The line goes through a hole in this scoop to a large treble hook and it is the scoop gripping the current that makes the tail waggle sexily, thus enticing a 'take'.

Kype – The 'hook' at the front of the lower jaw of a male salmon, which becomes more and more pronounced as the fish goes towards spawning time.

Left Hand Bank – The left hand bank as you look down a river, the way the water is flowing.

Lie – A salmon lie is a place where a salmon might stop and rest, say in front of or behind a large boulder that breaks the current in a river.
Should not be confused with:

Lie – Me telling you I caught the British Record Salmon (which I didn't).

Loch – A lake, possibly on a river.

Mending the line – Nothing to do with joining a parted line.
When you cast out across a river and you want your bait to fish slowly in order to give fish plenty of time to come for it, the river current at first will drag your line into a big downstream bend, pulling your fly across the river too fast.

Therefore you lift the nearest part of the line to you out of the water and flick it upstream so that the bend in the line is the opposite way, taking the current time to reverse, during which your bait comes fishing slowly across.

Middle of the River – A central point in the river which can be found, more often than not, at a point equidistant between the left and right hand banks.

Minister – A religious man, a bit like a Reverend.

Monster – A very, very large fish that is absolutely massive, huge, gigantic, colossal, gi-normous, humongous .....
Please use your imagination with the last two words.

Parr – A young salmon living in the river until going to sea as a smolt around the end of its second year.

Pool – 'Fishing hole' in North America. A place in the river where fish might rest and can be caught, normally delineated at the beginning and end by something like shallows, rocks or rapids, or possibly something on the river bank, like a big rock, a fallen tree, etc.
Pools are given different names to identify them and are quite easily fallen into.

Pratt – A silly person.

Reverend – A religious man, a bit like a Minister.

Right Hand Bank – The right hand bank as you look down a river, the way the water is flowing.

Rise – Not something you get out of someone after winding them up, but the splash made by a salmon having leapt from the water as it re-enters.

River Board – An organisation in charge of the management of a river.

Rod – A fishing rod. Fishing pole (North America).

Runner – A running fish, one that is travelling fast upstream.

Rusty Nail – A mixture of neat Drambuie and Whisky, not for the faint hearted. Could be beneficial massaged in, although I have never tried this and warn that you would be doing so at your own risk.

Sea Lice – When salmon enter fresh water they have small brown sea lice attached to them that drop off within some 72 hours, being unable to live in fresh water. These sea lice can have a long white tail, in fact a string of eggs, and this 'tail' drops off first, within some 24 hours. Therefore it is possible to tell roughly how long a fish has been in the river if it has sea lice on it, with or without the white tail.
Fish are called 'sea licers' when they have sea lice on them.
Whenever I was asked the slightly silly question as to whether we had really big fish in the Tay I would reply, "Well I wouldn't say our fish are that big, but I did have a sea lice on for quarter of an hour the other day!"

Sea Trout – A migratory brown trout family member that goes to the sea to feed and returns to the river to spawn. Perhaps the hardest fighting of British game fish they can be fished for with a small fly and great anticipation in the dead of night.

Shrimp and Prawn Fishing – It used to be perfectly legal to fish for salmon on the river Tay using shrimps and prawns, as had been practiced since before 1900. However as salmon stocks fell the Tay River Board quite rightly banned their use as they could be responsible for killing a lot of fish in certain river conditions.

Smolt – The stage a young salmon has reached as it makes its way to the sea for the very first time.

Spey Casting – The casting of a double handed fly rod so the fly line theoretically 'never' goes behind you. I found it the laziest, easiest form of casting, but most people will tell you what a great and extremely difficult and wonderful art it is.
These people are talking complete cobblers.

Spate – A flood (Scottish)

Sprats - a small sea fish, dyed pink, gold or plain silver as bait for salmon.

Springer – A spring salmon entering a river between January and May.

Swivel – Nothing to do with Elvis Presley. A small revolving metal device with an eye on either end of it tied between the main line and the final few feet of line leading to the lure which stops the main fishing line from kinking up due to the lure's spinning action.

Take – The 'take' is when a fish grabs your bait. 'Taking fish' are those that 'take' readily, as opposed to those you can fish for days for, but are not interested.
If a fish 'takes' you, but you fail to hook it this can be referred to as:
Getting a 'pull', a 'rug', a 'tug', a 'knock', a 'bump', a 'rattle', etc.
It can also result in loud usage of a variety of expletives.
The latter are common when failing to hook a fish that 'takes' you in the closing moments of a blank week.

Toby Spoon – A spoon is a metal lure that can be a variety of colours, the most common of which is pure silver. It is bent in the middle to make it wobble 'fish-like' and has a treble hook at the tail end.
The Toby Spoon was a great favourite.

Toff – A name given by ghillies to wealthy, supposedly high class people.

Trolling - Using oars or engine whilst having lures out 'trolling' behind you.

Trout – A wild Brown Trout, called a 'Brownie' or 'wee Tammy Troot' in Scotland.

Upstream – If you look 'up' a river, with the water flowing towards you, you are looking upstream.

You're on your own from now on. Good Luck!

Place Names:

Dunkeld – Dunkeld was the ancient capital of Scotland before Edinburgh and has its own Cathedral. It is a charming and vibrant village sitting surrounded by mountains on one side of the river Tay opposite the village of Birnam. The two are connected by Thomas Telford's 1809 bridge that marks the bottom of the Dunkeld House beat.
Dunkeld and Birnam are situated at the beginning of the Highland Fault (no, that is not **my** fault) twelve miles north of Perth and an hour or so north of Edinburgh.
In Shakespeare's MacBeth 'Three witches came from Birnam woods'.
I was acquainted with all three of them when I lived in Dunkeld.

Places referred to:

Perth – principal city of Perthshire situated on the river Tay just above the estuary.

Pitlochry – a lovely Perthshire town some 24 miles north of Perth on the river Tummel, the biggest tributary of the river Tay. The hydroelectric dam and fish ladder, with fish moving from tank to tank up and through the dam into Loch Faskally, is situated at Pitlochry. Best time to view fish doing this is in April/May.

Bankfoot – village on the old A9 road from Perth to Dunkeld.

Luncarty (Lunkerty) – village on the old A9 road from Perth to Dunkeld.

Names of Beats on the river Tay mentioned in this book:

The Dam Below the dam at Pitlochry.

Upper Dunkeld The beat above Dunkeld House beat.

Dunkeld House Dunkeld House Hotel beat - ends at Dunkeld bridge.

Murthly Murthly Estate, split into Upper & Lower Murthly beats.

Catholes Starts at the Catholes weir down near Stanley village.

Stanley Sometimes called Pitlochrie Pool or Stanley Mill.

Benchil Ben-kil, a lower beat just below Stanley.

Redgorton Upper and lower, again lower beats below Stanley.

Waulkmill Walk-mill or Waulkmill Ferry, a lower beat.

Names of some of the Pools on Beats mentioned:

Dunkeld House: From the top of the beat down to Dunkeld Bridge: March, Carrot Beds, Ivy Tree, Rock, Ferry, Lady, Cutty Stone, Grey Stone, Green Point, Mouse Trap, Girnal, Grotto, Gage Tree, Fifey, Cathedral, Sandy.

Murthly Estate: Burn Mouth, Girnal, Ministers, Firs, Boat, Sparriemuir

Stanley Mill: Corner, Pitlochrie, Kirky, Wash House, Horsey

Benchil: Aitken Head, Little Shot

Stobhall – Woodside, Stank End

<u>Names of Rivers</u>:

Beauly - River north of Inverness, running into the Beauly firth.

Braan – Tributary of the Tay that has the Hermitage Falls, impassable to salmon, and joins the Tay on the right hand bank above Dunkeld bridge.

Damph – Loch Damph, on the north west coast of Scotland at Torridon.

Earn - Confluent of the Tay joining at the top of the estuary.

Garry - High tributary of the Tay above Loch Faskally.

Glass – the river Glass north of Inverness.

Helmsdale – Fantastic river in far north east of Scotland.

Lochy – River draining the Great Glen flowing west to Loch Linnhe (sea loch) at Fort William.

Oykel – North East Scottish river running into the Dornoch Firth at Bonar Bridge.

Tay – Scotland's biggest and most prolific salmon river, comprising more than 1500 miles of rivers, lochs and tributaries. One of the big four Scottish rivers, the others three being Tweed, Dee and Spey.

Tummel – the biggest tributary of the river Tay. Loch Tummel is formed by the hydro-electric dam at Pitlochry, the river Tummel begins below the dam.

Background information on Ghillies mentioned:

Jimmy McLean – pronounced 'Ma-claine'.
One of the kindest, most knowledgeable, insightful and humorous people you could ever wish to meet.
Ghillie at Dunkeld House Hotel from the 1940's until he passed away in August 1983 at the age of 74.
Jimmy gave immense pleasure to countless people who fished with him over the years. He was an old style ghillie full of respect for those he took fishing who would find themselves immersed in wonderful conversations with a great raconteur as he whisked them off into a world of nature, fish and fishing. He was my great friend and mentor from when I first met him as a small boy and worked with my family after we purchased Dunkeld House in the winter of 1968 We enjoyed a multitude of wonderful and humorous sporting times together.

Jimmy MacDonald – Another wonderful old style ghillie who worked on Upper and Lower Murthly. He and I got on famously and had some hilarious fishing times together. He was a kind, caring man and a great friend.

Geordie Stewart – Ghillie on Catholes/Pitlochrie Pool.
Has seen more spring fish than most ghillies and really knows how to catch them. Great sense of humour.

Sandy Penney – Ghillie who finished his career on the lower beats of the Tay such as Waulkmill. Tremendous sense of humour and an excellent fly fisher as are most ghillies. We had a lot of laughs and great fishing together.

Alf Campbell – Ghillie who worked on many of the lower beats of the Tay and finished on Stobhall/Taymount. Alf was a good friend and a gentleman.

George MacInnes - Great Tay fisher who took a temporary ghillying job at Ballathie on the lower Tay for 1 year and stayed for 20 years!

Other ghillies – Sandy Winter, Bob Campbell, Colin Leslie.

Index

Your Notes

Glossary of Terms 1
1. The Pitlochry Poacher 12
2. Early Days 13
3. Like Father Like Son? 14
4. Close Call 15
5. The Ghost of the White Lady 16
6. Hooked! 18
7. Jock, Harry and the Viaduct 19
8. My First Fish 21
9. Spoilt for Choice 22
10. The Great Interrupter 23
11. Dram Fish 24
12. Forty Pounders 26

Jimmy McLean stories
13. Two Old Boys 27
14. The Elderly Farmer 28
15. Three Things 28
16. The Reverend 29
17. Autumn Leaves 30
18. As Nature Intended 30
19. A Fair or Unfair Day? 31
20. Jimmy's Secret 32

----

21. The Harbinger 32
22. Joe and the Monster 34
23. Mickey Mouse Reels 36
24. The Great Northern Diver 37
25. Vanishing Tay Trout 38
26. Eye Eye 40
27. The Greatest Schemes 41
28. Difficult Fish 42
29. Rick and the Monster 43
30. Hartley Byrom's Big Fish 45
31. Jack Charlton 47
32. The Wader-less Fisherman 48
33. The Bet 49
34. The Call of Nature 50
35. First Name Basis 51
36. Miss Ballantyne and The Ministers 52

Williams, Morris & Miller

37. Lord Sandwich.................................. 53
38. The Japs and the Dam Fish.............. 54
39. Not Big Enough................................ 55
40. My Wanger!....................................... 56
41. Kowalski... 58

On The Glass

42. Willie the Fish................................... 59
43. Dog Fly Days..................................... 60

----

44. Bill Met By Moonlight......................... 62
45. Helmsdale Hiatus.............................. 63
46. There Goes The Neighbourhood........ 65
47. Haow!.. 67
48. Old Willie.. 69
49. Unlikely Thieves................................ 71
50. Catalogue of Disaster........................ 72
51. The Desperadoes.............................. 73
52. Catholes.. 74
53. Expletives on the Wind...................... 75
54. Geordie and the WashHouse............ 77
55. Bob Campbell and Horsey................. 78
56. A Cargill Day...................................... 79
57. Fame at Last!..................................... 81
58. Low Water Flies................................. 83
59. The Prawn King.................................. 85
60. The Purple Prawn.............................. 87
61. The Length of Loch Tay..................... 90
62. Wedding Distraction.......................... 91
63. Big Fish Sprint................................... 92
64. Old Roy.. 94
65. Old John.. 94
66. Fly Over All.. 95
67. A Different Way.................................. 96
68. The Backing Up.................................. 96
69. Scotland's Secret Weapon................ 97
70. Winter Fishing.................................... 99
71. Jim and the Horsey Women..............100

Loch Damph
72. Ferox!.. 102
73. Iced Lollies.. 106
74. The Bait Ball.. 107
75. Ethereal Light.. 107

On The Piddle
76. The John Wayne Epic!........................ 108

Tales of Jake
77. Take a Dive.. 110
78. A Face Full of Salmon........................ 111
79. Fishing Games.. 112
80. The Flying Dog Cure........................ 113
81. Life Change.. 114

Tales of the Brigadier
82. Cast of a Lifetime........................ 115
83. The Great Wader........................ 116
84. Bowling Along........................ 116
85. Winning In The End........................ 116
86. Beating The System?........................ 117

Anecdotes
87. Who Needs Rods?........................ 119
88. Anchors Aweigh!........................ 119
89. Cobblers!.. 120
90. Cock of The North........................ 120
91. A Bit of Perspective........................ 120
92. A Seriously Big Fish........................ 121
93. Spray Day.. 122
94. Rock of Ages!........................ 123
95. April Fools.. 123
96. Space Launch........................ 124
97. Lost and Found........................ 125
98. Unstoppable Salmon........................ 125
99. A Bit of Shakespeare........................ 125
100. Help! Help!.. 126

Jess Miller's

True or False Fishing Stories 1

TRUE means did it actually happen, was it actually said?

1. The Pitlochry Poacher

There was a tale told long ago on the Upper Tay of an old poacher who practised his art on the river Tummel, one of his favourite places to poach being below the dam at Pitlochry.

It was said that he used piano wire on his stout rod and reel so he could haul any salmon he illegally hooked straight out of the river to make a quick getaway.

On one particular evening however it appeared he had hooked Moby Dick himself. Not only was he unable to haul the fish straight from the river as usual, but this time he found it was the salmon that was dictating the fight and not he.

For some three hours they fought each other until the evening light was almost gone.

The poacher's problem, apart from the risk of being caught, was that he was married to a redoubtable and extremely difficult woman who would take great pleasure in making his life absolute hell if he was not home soon.

With this in mind he hit upon an ingenious plan.

Backing away from the river and around a huge fir tree on the river bank, then moving to the downstream side of it, he jammed his rod firmly into the stone dyke that ran alongside the road to the dam.
Returning to the fish's side of the tree he grabbed a stout bough and began wrapping the taught piano wire around and around it until each time the great fish moved away across the river the bough would extend slowly after it. When the pressure became extreme the piano wire going back around the tree would even pull upon the rod as well and the bough and rod combined would gradually force the fish back again.
And so the old poacher went home, leaving the fish see-sawing the piano wire back and forth around the tree as it fought ever onwards.
That night the old poacher could do nothing but think about what might be going on up at the dam and in his mind he kept picturing the great fish pulling the huge bough out over the river and the tree and the rod gradually forcing the fish back again. He kept wondering what he might find in the morning and it was a long time before he was finally able to drift off to sleep.
Arriving back at the dam just before first light he expected to find either the fish gone, the piano wire parted, his stout rod shattered or perhaps the unlikely miracle of some huge great fish lying dead beside the river bank.
Instead he came upon the most astonishing sight.
He'd sawed the tree in half!

2. Early Days

In 1958 at the age of nine I graduated from fishing for roach, rudd and perch with bread paste under a float in ponds on Lancashire's Fylde and ventured onto Scotland's river Tummel, a tributary of the Tay, with my tiny gold spoon and a tin of maggots.
My sister and Jock, my father's driver, walked on to fish the main river, but I stayed behind on a tiny side stream under a canopy of trees.
It was full of small trout, and I mean small! I caught my very first trout and called Jock, we unhooked it and put it back, after which I caught several more. Then I went to see what the two of them were doing.
My sister had let her worm drift onto the sand at her feet and Jock suddenly noticed quite a large trout was nibbling at it and told her to strike.
She promptly launched the first brown trout satellite, which landed in the foliage behind us!
We were staying at the Atholl Palace hotel in Pitlochry, which was a bit of a disaster in those days so we looked for better accommodation.
We came across Dunkeld House Hotel and I met ghillie Jimmy McLean for the first time. He took us down to a spot above the Grey Stone croy one evening so we could sit waiting in high anticipation of seeing the otters that had made a mud slide on the opposite bank. As the light began to fail there they were, running up to the top of the bank, slithering all the way back down again and landing with a splash in the river.
They were having great fun and so were we watching them!

When we got better at casting Jimmy took us over to the island above the hotel one afternoon and we fished on the far side of it in the really fast water, spinning with glazed minnows which the big trout came for. My sister and I each caught a couple between one and a half and two and a half pounds and Jimmy cleaned and cooked them, right there on the island.
As we sat in the sun with the river rushing past us they seemed the most wonderful fish we had ever eaten.
These were the days that would forever hook me on fishing.

3. Like Father like Son?

My dad was not a fisherman, he was a successful businessman and we were a reasonably wealthy family, my dad owned a Rolls Royce.
We had a driver called Jock and it was with Jock at a very early age I had spent many hours fishing in ponds for elusive roach and rudd, but now it was Dunkeld House where I yearned to be.
In 1959 my father decided he would come to Scotland with us, which was quite surprising seeing as he was more suited to holidaying on the French Riviera.
One day during my dad's one and only trip to Scotland he decided to take my sister and I fishing. Many years later I tracked down the spot where we had fished, it was on the Aberfeldy road that runs alongside the upper Tay. With Jock driving and my father dressed immaculately as usual we rounded a bend and came upon several signs that read:
'No Fishing!'
'Poachers will be Prosecuted!'
'Private, No Trespassing!'
"This must be the place!" said my dad and we stopped, jumped out and got our fishing rods ready.
Jock parked the Rolls stealthily in the bushes and we crept down to the river. Hidden amongst the undergrowth my sister and I cast out small blue and silver metal Devons. Whack! The first trout hit me and it fought hard. When I got it in and netted it, it was a two pounder! My sister then caught one of a similar size and soon I caught another weighing a pound and half. The trout were queuing up to get at our Devons and we had caught three each when Jock spied a boat coming down the river and we made a run for the car.
Throwing everything into the car we jumped in and the Rolls was eased out of the bushes onto the road and we sped away.
This was the one and only time I ever went fishing with my dad!

4. Close Call

One day during one of our visits to Dunkeld House in 1959 we were moored off the Fifey bank, fishing into the Gage Tree pool. Nothing was happening and I was becoming more and more desperate to catch a salmon. Jimmy moved up to the bow to haul the anchor up and I asked if I could start the engine. He had shown me what to do and I went to the big Evinrude Fisherman outboard and grabbed the handle to give it a pull, but found I was not able to pull it very far at all.
So I pulled at it again and this time I did manage to turn the engine over. Determined to get it to start I planted my feet to get maximum purchase and gave it a real pull.
The resistance from the engine suddenly gave way and my momentum carried me backwards, straight over the gunwale of the boat into the fast flowing Tay!
It was such a shock hitting the water and I floundered about upside down in the current at the side of the boat, trying to find which way was up.
At the moment I thought I might die powerful hands gripped my clothes, hauled me to the surface and up into the air. I remember, as he shook the water out of me and turned me the right way up, hearing Jimmy's voice asking,
"And where do you think you're going?"
It had been a narrow squeak.
The powerful currents of the Tay had been seconds from taking me.
That was the day Jimmy McLean saved my life.

5. The Ghost of the White Lady

I was ten years old and had not yet caught my first salmon.
In those days the Tay seemed to me to be an ocean ruled by the king of fish, the Atlantic Salmon. As a youngster I became mesmerised by the wild brown trout and grayling that were abundant in the river, hardly daring to hope that one day I might actually come into contact with the king himself.
I would get pulled by and miss many trout or grayling in a day's fly fishing, get my fly cast caught up either on itself, on me, a bush or around the rod and sit for ages trying to undo the numerous fankles I got into and then quickly get back to fishing every minute that I could.
Out of such apprenticeship eventually comes a degree of competence.
After dinner one evening my mother said I could go and fish just above where the boat was beached at the front of the hotel and she would come down and get me when it was time to come in.
I almost ran down to the river, waded into the edge, cast out and straightaway I was into a trout. Next came a pound and a half Grayling, then I shook off some salmon parr and then more trout were at me as the evening rise got into full swing.

It was enthralling and engrossing. I made a little pool in the shingle to keep the four fish I had caught in and waded back into the edge of the river as the feeding fish boiled away as darkness approached.
Not being that keen on the dark I kept a look out over my shoulder for my mother's light coloured coat to appear a short distance away along the wire fence at the top of the high wall behind me. Eventually I could just make her out, coming along the high bank and shouted that I had caught four fish and one, a two and a half pound brown trout, was a really big one.
There was no reply, only the white of mother's coat as it came floating along the high bank towards me.
Suddenly I froze as a disturbing feeling came over me and the frightening realisation of how dark it was getting. This was made worse by the fact that if this truly was my mother she would surely have replied by now.
Still the white thing was coming drifting along the high bank and by now it was right behind me. My eyes were opened wide, staring at it in terror when a lilting female voice called out,
"Be careful, little boy, don't go out too far."
I looked down and the river was just about to come over the top of my thigh waders. Gingerly I backed out of the current, looked round again....and the white thing had vanished!
I stood there petrified, it was now so dark I could barely make out the river bank and the sudden loud screech of an owl close by did nothing to help ease my fear.
How long I was there I don't know, but eventually another whitish thing appeared just above me and my mother enquired why I was standing out in the river facing the river bank.
By the time we got back to the hotel she had become as disturbed about what had happened as I was because she could see that I was terrified. There were only a few guests staying and they had either gone to bed or were in the bar or the hotel lounges and none of them were wearing a light coloured coat, nor was there one hanging on the hooks outside the cloakroom, nor had any guests been out for a walk.
Eventually it was decided it had not been anyone from the hotel, but also that the direction the 'person' had been going was away from the hotel and Dunkeld, where there was nothing for miles.
I found this very disturbing!
Whoever or whatever it was the Ghost of the White Lady as she has become known had stopped me going out any further into the current that night and if I had I probably would not have been here today to recount these stories to you.
The Ghost of the White Lady saved my life.

6. Hooked!

Most anglers have hooked themselves at one time or another, some many times, though hopefully less as their competence increased.
The first time I stabbed myself with a hook was as a youngster back in the 1950's when, trying to cast to that tantalising trout rising way beyond my casting ability (a trout too far?), I succeeded in putting one of my team of flies straight through my ear lobe.
After my initial panic we cut the leader away, but had to leave the fly in as the barb had vanished. I was taken down to Dunkeld to visit Dr. Hepburn, a wonderful archetypal village doctor beloved of everyone in the locality.
A kindly man with a twinkle in his eye he examined me and said,
"Well, you've hooked a big one there alright, laddie. Nothing to worry about though, what we're going to do is cut away the fly's dressing with a razor blade so we can push it further through, then snip off the barb and pull the hook out. It won't hurt at all, so you just sit there and relax."
I have to admit that I wasn't that relaxed as too many doctors and dentists had already told me during my short existence they weren't going to hurt me and promptly had done so.
However as Dr.Hepburn worked away he asked me about the river and the trout fishing to take my mind off what he was doing, but I never felt anything, just as he had said. With the hook bared he pushed it further through, then snipped off the barb with a pair of pliers, pulled the hook out and dabbed something on the tiny hole.
With my major hospital procedure over he walked me to the door and said,
"It must be busy out there on the river, that's the third today!"
When this kindly village doctor passed away more than 1000 people came to his funeral.

7. Jock, Harry and the Viaduct

We lived in St.Annes-on-Sea in Lancashire and I was some nine or ten years old when my father's driver, Jock, introduced me to his friend Harry Yates and we drove up to some lakes near the river Lune to go pike fishing.
Harry was a tall, gangling man who wore National Health spectacles and seemed friendly.
Jock was a good fisherman as apparently was Harry.
I, on the other hand, had never even seen a pike and was full of anticipation, not knowing what to expect.
I remember Jock setting live fish under a big float which moved one way and then another as a pike apparently circled around it, but nothing happened. Something did happen to me however when a Jack pike grabbed the red and gold Devon I was spinning.
I was in awe of the look of it as Jock unhooked the three pound fish, showed me its teeth and we slipped it back into the lake.
After that we went to do what Jock and Harry were really there for.
Lord Peel's stretch of the Lune has a huge, famous pool on it called the Viaduct Pool. As we walked down the railway line towards it we came out on top of the viaduct and in the tail of this great pool below us we could see lots of huge salmon lying in row upon row.
I was totally fascinated.
Jock went down to the river and Harry spotted for him as he threw out a pink Spratt with Harry trying to guide him to get it as close as possible to a particularly big salmon.
I didn't know it, but we were poaching!
As the afternoon wore on Harry spotted someone walking along the river bank in the distance and we left and drove home.
I was told I shouldn't say anything about this 'salmon fishing' to my parents.
Before long Jock and Harry went back to the Viaduct pool and Jock told me the story.
They had arrived very early on a Sunday morning and had gone about trying to capture the king of the river in exactly the same way with Jock down below, spinning various colours of Sprats at the fish lying under the viaduct, but to no avail.
After a while Harry had tied up a prawn and proceeded to fish it from the top of the viaduct, casting it well up into the pool below and then drifting it back through the fish. It wasn't long before one took it and a good fish at that. It took off down the river under the viaduct with Harry hanging on determinedly, his rod bent right round under the bridge. He hooked his feet over the nearest rail of the railway track behind him for fear of losing his balance and falling over the edge of the parapet, in which case the fish would have won!
Then the train appeared.
Harry took one look at it, saw it was on the other track and held on grimly whilst it came thundering past. Jock said that looking up at Harry battling with the fish, which was now leaping and thrashing about downstream of the viaduct whilst the train rocketed past him had been extremely funny, but not for poor Harry.
Eventually he got the fish to come back up into the pool where Jock gaffed the big twenty five pounder and they quickly left for fear of being apprehended.

Apparently Harry had been white and shaking for some time due to his experience on the viaduct and not far down the road the salmon, which they thought they had dispatched properly, started banging around in the boot of the car, so they had to stop to complete the job.
I never saw Harry Yates again and soon Jock lost his job with us.

8. My First Fish

On the 10th April 1961 at the age of 12 and after 3 years of trying I caught my first fish.
It was an eleven pounder that took a spoon harled from the boat in the Gage Tree pool, shortly followed by a ten and a half pounder over in the Fifie.
I was 'blooded', an age old custom in salmon fishing, and wore daubs of dried blood on my cheeks and forehead for the rest of the day.
People saw the blood and congratulated me, now I was a salmon fisherman!
And on the very next day and on the same Kynoch Killer I caught a twenty four pounder!
I was on my own with Jimmy and played it on the Hardy County spinning rod and Hardy Exalta reel my parents had given me. The fish first made strong runs before going deep to sit on the bottom, then it began jumping and running all over the pool. It took me forty minutes to land, after which Jimmy said it had shown me absolutely everything a salmon could do and that I had learned all I needed to know to be able to fight a big fish.
We went back to the hotel in the autumn of that year and on September 5th my sister, my mother and I walked up to the Rock Pool, at the top of the beat and my mother sat on the bank whilst we launched our lures out into the pool. I was fishing high up on the bend in the quieter water and nearly jumped out of my skin when my blue, red and silver Toby spoon was grabbed by what turned out to be a twenty three pound salmon! My sister was fourteen and I was twelve and we had never caught a salmon from the river bank. I fought the fish as Jimmy had taught me back in the spring and when it came in my sister gaffed it and we hauled it ashore and dispatched it. The three of us stood there in amazement of our feat as we washed the great salmon off.
But now we had to carry it back to the hotel, which was a long way!
We did our best, but after a while we had to lay it on my mother's jacket and drag it or we were never going to get there.
Mother never forgot having to wash and wash that jacket to get rid of the smell!
The following morning instead of going fishing everyone seemed to be content to just stand around talking and I was itching to get down to the river, so I went.
I walked out on the gravel in front of the hotel and threw out my Toby spoon. After a few casts I hooked a fish, played, landed and dispatched it and walked back up with an eight pounder. They were all still there talking, standing by the garages behind the hotel and were astonished when I produced the fish.
Now I had caught two fish from the river bank and my first on my own.
Dunkeld House had grown into more than Valhalla for me.

Little did I know it, but in the winter of 1968 we would buy the hotel and live right there on the river that I loved for seventeen years.

9. Spoilt for Choice

As a 12 year old in 1961 I stood on the front steps of Dunkeld House Hotel with ghillie Jimmy McLean and watched as a huge Rolls Royce swept down the drive, swung around the lone central tree that dominated the car park and eased to a stop in front of us, a mass of gleaming chrome, polished two-tone brown paintwork and an engine whispering its power.

As we looked in admiration at the Rolls the driver got out and hailed Jimmy.

"McLean, I've got something fantastic to show you," he announced and we followed him around to the car's boot, which he unlocked with a flourish and lifted the tailgate.

This revealed a large brass bound teak box, like a small trunk, and the man bent to unlock it and lift the lid.

Upon doing so multiple rows of cantilever trays shot out in all directions, all crammed full of fishing lures and tackle. He pulled open three or four drawers and it seemed the entire boot of the Rolls had been turned into a fishing tackle shop!

I gazed at the rows of colourful Devons, Lucky Louie's, Spoons, Flies, Bottles of Sprats and Prawns and there were reels, hooks, leads, swivels and so much other tackle it was unbelievable. I remember seeing the names 'Hardy' and 'Farlow' on the packets of traces and fly casts.

Jimmy bent to inspect it all, moving his hand over the trays, I presumed he was checking to see if there was anything missing.

The two of them discussed the tackle at some length, its owner obviously so proud of his new emporium, until finally Jimmy proceeded to remove a large salmon fly from his lapel.

"Well, it's all very nice, but there's nothing in there we'll be using this week, this is what the fish are taking just now."

The man stood there with his mouth open and his ego in tatters, but that was the fly they went fishing with and that was the fly they caught fish with that week!

10. The Great Interrupter

Robert Despagne from Liege in Belgium used to fish at Dunkeld House with Jimmy McLean and became a good friend to me over the years. Robert was quite a character who would cover the bodywork of his new Porsche in Vaseline and never clean it, apart from the windows, during the two or three years that he would keep it. The Vaseline would become hard, but surprisingly his car didn't look too bad.

The method in his madness was proved when it came time to sell it.

A steam power clean of the bodywork would bring it back to new condition and he would get top price for it!

On one occasion he and Jimmy had entered the hotel bar before lunch having finished fishing for the morning and Jimmy, a great raconteur, was telling a gathering of several people one of his stories. Although he spoke some English Robert was unable to follow the tale and quickly got bored.

After a while Robert reached across to the far lapel of Jimmy's jacket, in which were hooked quite a number of salmon and trout flies.

"Jimmee! Jimmee! Good fly? Good fly?"

Having had his story interrupted Jimmy patiently explained which species of fish the fly was for and that it did indeed catch fish before resuming his storytelling.

As the story waned on though Robert became restless again and soon reached across and grabbed one of the other flies on Jimmy's lapel.

"Jimmee! Jimmee! Good fly? Saumon, er, sallmon?"

Once again with patience Jimmy explained about the fly and when it was a good time of the year to fish it before resuming his story, which was by now heading towards its climax. After a few minutes more, as Jimmy sat there with his arms outstretched demonstrating something critical to the hiatus of his tale, Robert made his final interruption and grabbed a big, bright hairy fly that was stuck in Jimmy's lapel.

"Jimmee! Jimmee! What is thees fly for?"

Having now had the punch line of his story completely ruined Jimmy looked down at the fly Robert was clutching onto, looked at me with a twinkle in his eye and said, "Tourists!"

11. Dram Fish

David Morris and I once set out for a day's harling in the boat at Dunkeld House with Jimmy McLean. It was the 13th October 1971.
The three of us were quietly excited because a long summer drought had ended and the river was cleaning after a flood and coming into prime condition. Surely the fish that had been held up in the estuary and lower beats of the river by the low water would come through in numbers on their way to the spawning grounds and we would get a chance at them?
We set out excitedly and in good humour fishing Kynoch Killers on the two spinning rods and a roving prawn out in the centre on a big fly rod and commenced harling from the front of the hotel as the river was too high for the upper part of our beat to hold fish.
We saw and caught nothing.
We didn't get a pull at the Cutty Stone, which was unusual, nothing at the Grey Stones, nor at Green Point or the Mouse Trap, nor after we rounded the corner high above Dunkeld Bridge and fished the Girnal. We were bemused to be fishing a seemingly empty river and could hardly believe we weren't seeing fish running in these almost perfect conditions. Mind you the river had been pretty dirty the day before and it still had a slight peaty stain to it.
But surely that wouldn't stop fish coming forward?
"There's one!" I proclaimed with relief.
"Where is he?" asked Jimmy.
"He's just come through the bridge into the Sandy, left hand arch. There's another one!"
And here they came, hundreds of fish running together having left the great holding beats below us probably at the same time as we had left the shingle beach in front of the hotel and now they were rising left, right and centre as they came through the distant bridge.
We met them at the Gage Tree and took two twelve pounders one after the other. Relieved to have at last opened the scoring we had a dram of whisky for each fish. It had been that lean a summer.
As we got into the Cathedral Stream, some three hundred yards above Telford's bridge, fish came piling on one after another, fighting hard in the big water. We took six up to sixteen pounds and continued, with six more large drams inside us, into the Sandy Pool which begins at the railings below Dunkeld Cathedral.
Here I got into a twenty one pounder that really went to town in the strong stream, followed by a thirteen pounder with David getting a ten pounder. We had a bloody large dram for the twenty one pounder. Each time we had a fish on we were concerned whether it would turn out to be a 'dram fish' or not. Would it fall off?
A few of them did and so these we could not celebrate with whisky.
Fish were coming through the bridge fast and furious as we ran for home and lunch with eleven fish on board and eleven drams inside us, a very big day on a beat that used to average one hundred fish for the entire year.
Jimmy had perhaps joined us in only half of the whiskies, he hardly ever drank on the river and almost never drank to excess anyway.
We had a quick lunch and came straight back out.

Arriving at the Cutty Stone the roving prawn on the centre rod received a bump, then another, then a strong pull, a rug, a tug and then........nothing.
A minute or two later Jimmy made the suggestion that from then on he would have a dram for every fish that came to the prawn; but didn't stick on, if that was alright with the two of us?
We said it was fine and settled down to see how much whisky we were going to be able to consume and how little Jimmy was going to get that afternoon.
At the Grey Stone croy a fish attacked the prawn and left it. Jimmy had a dram.
The same thing happened at Green Point that had Jimmy wishing us good health, wealth and prosperity.
"We'll get one in a minute, Mr.McLean," I said as David and I laughed nervously about how these three fish had behaved with the prawn.
All the way down the straight to the bridge if one fish came and pulled the prawn and didn't stick on, more than a dozen did and each time Jimmy had a dram, of course constantly and 'most sincerely' wishing us both well.
Some of the attempted takes were beyond belief with fish bumping and banging the prawn and chasing it all the way across the river, but not actually taking it.
David and I finally got one fish each down in the Cathedral Stream and the Sandy, but still there were fish after fish coming and banging the prawn. However Jimmy announced he had consumed enough whisky, which was gracious of him seeing as the bottle was now empty.
On account of this being the only time I ever saw him remotely merry with drink on the river I took over the motor and we made our way back upstream to the hotel.
If you had asked David and I to put money on what was going to occur with the prawn that afternoon you would have taken every penny off us. If we hadn't seen it with our own eyes we would scarcely have believed it. My error was that I had not noticed the day had changed, the overhead conditions had broken away from a greyish blanket of high cloud into bright sun with scudding white cloud, the river had cleaned that little bit more and fish had taken to running hard, whereas in the morning they had been coming forward slowly and steadily, allowing us to make something of them.
But the years of experience of a canny Scottish ghillie had quickly spotted the change and consequently gained him his reward, delivered with such consistency by so many 'dram fish' that had harried, but had never taken, the roving prawn we fished that afternoon.

12. Forty Pounders

The two biggest fish from Dunkeld House Hotel water during the seventeen years of our tenure up to 1985 were 42 and 44 pounds and both were caught by the same man - five years apart!
Mr. and Mrs.Corben-Brown used to fish with Jimmy every autumn.
He was a tall man, his wife diminutive and over the years she became more and more demanding of Jimmy, who would not exactly moan to me about her, he was never a moaner, but he occasionally would tell me the little niggling things she had him running around doing.
The 42 pounder, taken on a Kynoch Killer harled from the boat in the Gage tree pool on the 29th September 1969, gave her husband a long fight, but stayed with them in the pool luckily. With fish of this size it's simply a question of wearing them down. For at least the first half of the fight the fish is in control and then, gradually, control swings the way of the angler as the fish slowly tires.
Even so the hooks could come away right at the end and many big fish have been lost in those final seconds, many as they rolled onto their sides at the surface, changing the angle of pressure on the hooks.
A big autumn cock fish, dark and red with a huge head and kype (the upright part at the front of the bottom jaw that develops in cock fish as they go towards spawning) it was a cause of big celebration, as a forty pound class fish would be anywhere on the river system.
Jimmy was delighted about it and he and Corben-Brown posed for pictures with the fish on the lawns in front of the hotel.
It was during the five years before the next big fish came along that Mrs.Corben-Brown became more and more arthritic and Jimmy had to just about carry her in and out of the boat.
But he was not convinced about her arthritis being as bad as she made it out to be and was exasperated at being made to run around after her for all kinds of fairly insignificant things, although he never complained.
So the 3rd October 1974 arrived and he set off with the Corben-Browns to harl their way down the river from the hotel. Arriving at Green Point they hooked a fish on a 'roving' prawn fished on the big central fly rod. Jimmy tied the boat to the bank and Mr.Corben-Brown announced that the fish was probably no more than ten pounds the way it was playing. Jimmy said he should have known something was up as at one point a large boil could be seen on the surface in the middle of this deep pool and no ten pounder could have made such a boil.
The fish made off down the river then swung into the bank below them and came cruising up towards them just a couple of yards off the bank and saw the boat at the same moment that Jimmy saw the fish and realised the great size of it. Without hesitation he told the two in the boat to 'look out!' and stuck a long handled gaff into the fish as it turned to go back out into the main stream and he began to haul it aboard.
It was a huge black and red autumn cock fish, exactly the same as the one five years earlier, with a massive head, nose and kype. For years afterwards Jimmy loved to tell the story of the arthritic Mrs.Corben-Brown who, upon seeing this

massive, ugly head of the beast coming over the gunwale at her, took off out of the boat and up the bank like a greyhound!
For the capture of this great fish Jimmy McLean won the ABU Tay Ghillie of the Year award for 1974, of which he was immensely proud.
The pity was that ABU ceased presenting the award some years later.
This was sad as it had brought together ghillies from the highest tributaries of the Tay system with those on the lowest, most prolific beats of the river to exchange knowledge and build friendships that otherwise wouldn't have happened. Still Jimmy and Mr.Corben-Brown had taken their place in the salmon fishing history of the river Tay.

Jimmy McLean stories

13. Two Old Boys

Two old boys from Glasgow fished with Jimmy one day in the 1950's.
They fished with large Mitchell fixed spool sea reels and one spring day they got down into the Cathedral Stream, harling above Dunkeld Bridge, when one of the rods bent double as a big spring fish came on.
One of the two old boys picked it up to find the fish was making downstream for Perth at a furious rate.
Screwing the drag up on the reel to try and stop it the tiniest wisp of smoke seemed to come off the guide on the bale arm of the reel and the line parted.
The second old boy chastised the first, telling him in no uncertain manner that he had been both foolish and ridiculous for letting a big salmon get away and a serious argument erupted between the two over the lost fish.
Fishing resumed and they let their lines away as Jimmy took the boat a little way up river and began to fish it down again.
Wham! In almost exactly the same place the other old boy's rod bent double and he picked it up only to find the same thing was happening to him.
Whatever he tried to do was to no avail as the fish made off straight down the river through the bridge and broke the line.
There ensued the most almighty argument between the two of them with copious amounts of mud slinging as Jimmy sat witness knowing full well that two seriously big springers had drawn into the pool above the run at the Holly Bush and that neither man would have landed either of them as they took off through the bridge in the direction of the Atlantic.

14. The Elderly Farmer

There was once an elderly farmer who suddenly got the urge for sex when out ploughing his fields one day.

Rushing back to the farm house he yelled to his wife to get up to the bedroom, but by the time she had done so his urge had disappeared.

He chastised his wife and told her that if she ever saw him rushing in from the fields again she should get up to their bedroom and get herself ready.

Some weeks later the farmer's wife was looking out of their kitchen window when she saw her husband coming at great pace in from the fields towards the house.

Remembering what he had said she ran up to their bedroom and got ready.

The farmer burst through the front door calling her name, she answered from the bedroom so he bounded up the stairs two at a time, took one look at her lying in readiness on the bed and shouted,

"Get out of that you sexy bitch, the roof's on fire!"

15. Three Things

Jimmy used to have a saying: 'There are three things Scotland would be better off without. Factors, Ministers and Hoodie Crows!'

16. The Reverend

The Reverend at Dunkeld Cathedral back in the fifties was nicknamed 'the Crow' by the locals as he had a big 'beak' nose, reminiscent of a crow's beak.

A visitor who was looking for him one day stopped in the village square and asked one of the locals where the vicar could be found.
"Oh, you mean the Crow," said the local and happily gave directions.
The Reverend opened his door to the visitor to be asked if he was by chance Reverend Crow!

17. Autumn Leaves

Dunkeld House was bought from the Dowager Duchess of Atholl by a Captain Anderson and his wife after World War II.
One autumn Jimmy came in from fishing to find that the Captain had spent most of the day sweeping the front lawns clear of leaves and he proudly showed off his accomplishment.
"You needn't have bothered, there'll be an Easterly wind blowing tonight," said Jimmy.
Sure enough the wind blew strong from the East that night and the following morning the lawns were covered in masses of fallen leaves again.
Captain Anderson was distraught.
"Nothing to worry about, Captain," said Jimmy, "the wind will blow from the North West tonight."
That night there blew a savage Nor'Wester and the following morning nearly all of the leaves had been blown into the river.
The Captain had learned the lesson that more often than not nature looks after itself.

18. As Nature Intended

Two female students went fishing with Jimmy one day, both of them being enthralled by and in love with nature.
Jimmy McLean was a most knowledgeable man about everything to do with nature and all things living or growing and he kept the two of them spellbound, telling them in great detail about everything around them.
Down in the Gage Tree pool as they harled close to the bank a little water vole came swimming up the bank side. The two girls froze, their eyes glued to the vole as Jimmy told them all about it, how it lived and what it ate.
Then he let out a special sounding low whistle, upon which the water vole shot into the bank and disappeared.
The two girls looked to Jimmy for some explanation of this astonishing behaviour.
"Aye," said Jimmy, "and they don't come when you whistle!"

19. A Fair or Unfair Day?

A young man fished with Jimmy and me in the boat one day.
We didn't catch any fish that spring morning, but we saw a couple down in the Fifey, above the point at which the river Braan enters the Tay above Dunkeld Bridge.
During big water fish would come out of the Cathedral Stream onto the Fifey shallows on the right hand bank where they could get some peace from the strong stream. They often rose as they entered the tail of the pool and a really big fish did so as we harled our way down the pool.
The young man was dumbstruck at this explosion of water, never having seen a big salmon rise before.
Jimmy leaned forward with a pencil in his hand.
"Would you put a cross on the side of the boat where that one rose so we can come back to the same place and try to catch him again later?" he enquired of the young man. I gave Jimmy as sarcastic a look as I could as our young friend painstakingly made a big cross on the top of the gunwale.
Shortly he asked Jimmy very stiffly and properly if he could have the pleasure of pouring him a dram from a bottle of whisky he had specially purchased for this important day.
Jimmy said that would be most welcome, which was fairly unusual of him as he hardly ever drank on the river and he was being polite, so the bottle was duly produced. But just before he poured the whisky into the waiting glass we were amazed as our friend stopped and a sudden air of dejection came over him.
"I'm so sorry, Jimmy, I've forgotten the water and I know that highland ghillies always take water with their whisky. What a terrible mistake to make. I am so sorry. You're not offended are you?"
It was obvious this likeable young man was taking his first day fishing for salmon in a boat on the Tay so very seriously that Jimmy and I backed off with the kidology.
"No matter," said Jimmy, "I'm most certainly not offended and I appreciate your kind offer, but I'll survive without it you know, especially if we get a fish."
At this our friend brightened. But in a while we could see him studying that cross he had made on the side of the boat. All the way as we ran the boat back up the river at lunchtime he was studying it and just before we beached the boat he had a sort of hesitant half smile on his face and was looking at Jimmy, who was smiling back at him.
"You got me there, Jimmy! Put a cross on the side of the boat! That was brilliant!"
He began laughing at being the butt of the joke and falling for such a ridiculous thing.
"But with your cross we'll be able to find the place where that big fish was when we come back out in the afternoon!" said Jimmy and now all three of us were laughing.
"And by the way," McLean was about to deliver the coup de grace, "about forgetting the water to go with the whisky."
"Yes?" said our friend, suddenly becoming serious again.
Jimmy looked out across the swirling currents of the Tay and said,

"We've been floating about on quite a lot of it this morning you know."
The man who came out to fish with us that afternoon was a very different person. He had completely relaxed, realising he was with people who had a sense of humour and he turned out to have quite a sense of humour himself!

20. Jimmy's Secret

At Jimmy McLean's funeral in 1983 one of his friends told me that when Jimmy had been a young man, working in Glen Artney deer forest as a deer stalker, he had been attacked by his own black Labrador one day as he sat out on the hill eating his lunch.
The dog had suddenly gone berserk, attacked him and bit him in the shoulder, hanging on with no intention of letting go. After a struggle Jimmy had been able to reach his shotgun and had managed to shoot the dog, but he'd only just made it off the hill with great loss of blood, his shoulder scarred for life.
In the twenty five years I knew him Jimmy never once mentioned this to me.

----

21. The Harbinger

I am not keen on fishing low water drought conditions.
I'll fish in a drought, but give me a river that is high and I'm happy even if I catch nothing because I know fish are running, getting to where they are supposed to be going in the river system by spawning time.
Raking around for fish stuck in low water pools has never been my favourite pastime.
More than forty years ago I saw something I would see repeated a number of times down the years and learned the importance of its message.
It was the harbinger, the one who signals the coming rains.
It was at a time when the Tay was a sad looking, drought ridden river, her rocky, now bleached bones at the mercy of the sun's rays.
In Green Point we could read the inscribed low water marks on the great stone deep down under the right hand bank and the level was close to the record low.
It was so hot our shirts burned our backs.
All down the river green slime festooned what should have been clean, river-washed shingle and rock and if we tried to spin even our smallest lures, long, green weed would foul our hooks. So we fished small flies on trout rods, but even the trout were hidden as deep as they could go in their rocky hideouts, most probably gasping for breath in the high water temperature.
Our beat remained empty, listless and lifeless in the heat wave.
The drought had been on for months as we sat moored on the edge of the Fifey bank, now risen completely out of the water, and looked at stones sticking out of the Cathedral Stream where normally none showed. I hated it. Jimmy and I talked

of good times past and good times to come as we spent the sultry, burning days together. It was hard on him because he had no guests to take fishing as everyone who was booked that summer had cancelled, so we fished together as best we could.
As we sat having our lunch in the boat, looking out across the water towards the Cathedral an image of a fish, quite obviously a mirage, suddenly appeared in mid-air right in front of us, making a running jump. A grilse of four or five pounds, pure silver and in spanking condition splashed back into the river well forward of where it had come out and disappeared. I blinked a couple of times, remaining frozen, holding half a sandwich to my mouth. No, of course it hadn't been real. It had definitely been a mirage. I had simply been seeing things. After the long drought the heat was finally getting to me.
I hadn't seen a fish for months.
There was no way that fish could have been real.
Jimmy looked slowly around the river and drew in a long, deep breath, as if smelling the air. Then he looked at me and said,
"Rain coming."
Rain? Had he gone completely mad? It was hotter than hell and pure blue above us with not a cloud to be seen. I queried his observation.
"He knows," replied Jimmy nodding in the fish's direction, "we'll have rain before long, you wait and see."
He seemed in those moments to somehow have changed within himself, to have completely relaxed due to his new found knowledge.
How well he knew the harbinger and the message it brought of old.
That night I eagerly watched the weather forecast on television, but there was only the same hot weather over us and a front so far out across the Atlantic it was of little consequence. The following day Jimmy seemed to have forgotten all about the little grilse as he never mentioned it. I looked at the lawns around the hotel, burned and bare, and wished the rain really would come.
I would rather have been fishing a ten foot brown flood than this.
It was two nights later in the very early hours of the morning that I was half wakened by the rustling of stoats chasing mice amongst the crisp, dried leaves outside my window. I drifted off, but their noise came again, so I turned over and tried to go back to sleep. The crackling continued and so, after a while of drifting in and out of sleep, my brain finally asked the question whether stoats actually hunt in large packs and I began to listen to the noise.
The rustling was consistent, a bit too consistent for night hunters. So I got up, switched on the light, went to the window and held out my hand, only to have a large drop of water land on it!
Rain! Rain lads! It's raining! Don't panic! Get the fishing gear! Get dressed! Get going! Do!...Not!...Panic!
I found myself running around like a lunatic, pulling my chest waders on before three o'clock in the morning. Realising the futility of what I was doing I took them off and began to service my reel. I put new eighteen pound breaking strain line on it and went through all of my tackle, sorting everything out that I would need. By now the crackling was getting louder and before four o'clock, in the pitch dark, I headed out of my cottage for the river.

Why I didn't know, but it was better to be out in any kind of weather than what we had been suffering for the last few months.
It was raining hard by now and I was loving it.
I got down to the Gage Tree, put my rod and my gear down and sat there on the river bank as the rain started hammering down, roaring on the surface of the river.
We were going to make it! We were going to have an autumn to fish after all!
The harbinger had been right.
He had known full well the rain was coming some 72 hours beforehand and had been running into what would soon be a rising river.
And that's why he's always worth keeping an eye out for.

22. Joe and the Monster

For many years Joe Elliot was Head Keeper on the high ground estate of Drumour, by Trochry just a few miles west of Dunkeld. He was both a hard and hardy man, a great shot, deer stalker and salmon fisher and in his earlier days had done a lot of pike fishing and netting up on Loch Tay. He used to tell me stories about the huge pike he had dealt with up there.
Drumour was a great grouse shooting estate, much of which would be planted with trees by the Midland Bank Investment Trust, ensuring that 10,000 acres of the finest Scottish grouse moor was lost.
Eventually Joe's years at Drumour came to an end and he came to work with us at Dunkeld House from 1980 as our second ghillie, helping anglers on the riverbank.
Joe made his own Devon Minnows. He could turn them out of metal, but preferred working with wood. He would weight, size and colour them to exactly what he knew fish would take at certain times of the year and in certain river conditions. He used to supply me with the ones I needed and I caught many fish with them.
One autumn in the early 1980's the Tay was running high and had a dirty stain running through it as the rains continued. The river has a massive catchment area that occupies most of the middle of Scotland and the river system itself totals some 1500 miles or more of rivers, lochs and tributaries.
The rivers above us kept coming into flood with the persistent autumn rain and so the main Tay was unable to clean and ran with whatever colour was being washed in from somewhere higher up.
Joe found that the brightest colour of Marigold Yellow was the only one that worked. The fish could not really see other colours, or were not interested in them, but they could see and were definitely interested in his Marigold Devons. He began making them three to four inches long and painting them two tone Marigold with a lighter, brighter, pale yellow on one side. If you held one in the river and let it sink away as it spun round and round you could see it for quite a way, whereas a red Devon disappeared from sight almost immediately.
We caught some good fish that autumn on Joe's Marigold Devons.
It was his day off when he surprisingly appeared on the river bank at Dunkeld House. I knew him well and could see that something was clearly wrong. He seemed sort of exasperated, disturbed. This was a man who had escaped from German prisoner of war camp twice during World War II and had ended up in a

prison like Colditz. I had never seen him in any kind of state other than being completely organised and in control.
Joe knew John Carr of Doncaster very well, who owned the Upper Dunkeld beat above us, and had permission to go and fish on Carr's beat below the 'new' bridge that crosses the Tay above Dunkeld. On the left hand bank below the bridge lies the great ClachanTaggart stone some yards out into the river. In low water you can walk to it along a line of stones that remain submerged once the river rises. There is a lovely strong stream that runs next to this big stone and Jimmy and I would often look up the river to see big fish rising next to it, making huge splashes. When he saw fish showing at it Jimmy would tell me he could see those two famous Scottish comedians 'Clach' and 'Taggart' performing.
Joe had begun to fish his three inch Marigold Devon with a large weight on it up above this big stone and before long had hooked his all time monster fish.
He held his hands apart when he described the size of its head to me, which seemed to have been more than two feet long!
He'd had the fish in next to him and told me its size was inestimable, it had been huge. I knew he had seen many forty pound class salmon over the years as he used to fish the Tay's finest beats as a guest of his shooting clients, so I asked him if the fish had been in the fifty pound region. He looked at me for a minute, seemingly unable to speak, and there was the hint of a tear at the corner of his eye. He didn't answer my question, from which I gathered the fish had probably been well in excess of that figure.
He told me that early on in the fight the fish had suddenly taken off in a flash right across to the other bank at this wide part of the river. Fortunately it had stayed with him. Had it cleared out downstream he may well have lost it as, after a couple of hundred yards, trees and brush on the river bank would have stopped him from following it. Gradually the fish swam back over to his bank, as if to take a look at him, and that is when Joe had seen the huge bulk of it lying at the edge of the stream right next to him as if unconcerned by all the pressure he was applying.
Then it had sped across to the other bank again, but this time made off downstream. Joe followed but three quarters of his line had already disappeared and he admitted to me that in that moment he panicked.
This was so unlike the man I was startled by his admission.
He gave the great fish too much stick and his line parted.
I stood with him for a long time as we talked about what had happened. He'd had the fish on for two hours and by that time was convinced he'd had a good chance of landing it. He described the fish to me again in detail, particularly the size of its head. He had never seen a fish that came anywhere near the size of this one. Gradually he relaxed a bit and seemed less rattled, but all the same we both knew a man of his age would never be likely to hook such a monster again. It had been the fish of a lifetime.
The following day was October 15th, the last day of the season, and I walked down to the Gage Tree pool in the darkness at 6.00a.m. to wait for first light and fish a long day before hanging up my rods for the winter.
Joe was there before me.
He was standing motionless, looking out over the river.

I greeted him gently and we talked. He told me he had been unable to sleep and had been standing there for many hours unable to think about anything other than the great fish he had lost.

23. Mickey Mouse Reels

Do you remember when the first Red Ambassadeur multiplying reels appeared?
The ghillies on the Tay nicknamed them 'Mickey Mouse Reels' because they were difficult to get used to and consistently overran, producing large 'birds nests' of billowing line around the drum, the only solution to which very often would be to chop the line up and pull it off the reel bit by bit.
I'm sure you remember!
I was in the fishing room at Dunkeld House one afternoon back then when a fisherman came in from the river with a massive birds nest of line surrounding his Ambassadeur. I took one look at it and began to cut the 'hanks' of line away as he told me that some chap had come down the river and enquired of him whether that was one of those new Ambassadeur reels he'd been hearing about.
Upon confirmation that it was the man had asked if he could have a go with it.
The obliging angler had handed his rod over only to watch in horror as the man swung the rod back and put his full power into the cast, lashing the bait out at such a furious rate it had immediately produced the birds nest overrun I was now dealing with.
I was setting the reel up with a new line when another fisherman came in from the river with exactly the same problem. What threw us was that he proceeded to tell the same story about someone having asked to have a go with his Ambassadeur and having produced the same result!
We were working out from his description that it must have been the same man when yet a third fisherman appeared, in precisely the same predicament and telling precisely the same story!
I thought about the perpetrator of all these birds nests going into his local pub that night regaling his pals about how he'd 'done all the toffs' at Dunkeld House with their 'Mickey Mouse Reels'.
But I never found out who he was.

24. The Great Northern Diver

Loch Ordie lies a few miles from Dunkeld along a track that passes through the southern end of Atholl Estates.
There is a Loch Ordie dapping fly I have used with success on occasion, but I am not sure if it is named after this particular loch. Jimmy suggested we should fish it one summer's evening and talked about the times he had fished it in the past and the trout it had produced as we wound our way up the track in the Land Rover and through a number of padlocked gates.
As with most Scottish lochs the setting is picturesque.
Higher ground sweeps down to the loch and a low, lone fishing lodge, nestling with the higher ground behind it, stands to one side of the loch.
We pulled up in front of the fishing lodge and opened the back of the Land Rover to begin setting up our tackle. It was warm in the late afternoon sun and copious amounts of flies were hatching. Out on the loch trout were making ever expanding rings as they fed on the hatch.
Suddenly we could hear a gentle hissing sound. As it grew in volume we looked at each other and then up towards the roof of the lodge as a large bird, travelling at enormous speed, exploded into view.
He was a Great Northern Diver doing a superb imitation of a cruise missile.
His wings were tucked in tight to his body and his neck outstretched as he power dived past us, zipping along on the very shoulders of his wings with the air hissing from them.

We could see every feather on him he was so close and a fantastic sight he made. Passing us he was down onto the water in a second, snaking his way lazily across the loch just a couple of feet above it, and then rose slightly to go up over the distant headland and disappear.
In all he was in our sight for no more than fifteen seconds.
We were in awe of the speed the bird had been travelling at, over one hundred miles an hour at a guess, and amazed too at this kind of behaviour.
Jimmy said there was another loch high on the hill behind the fishing lodge and that was where he must have come from, but neither of us were sure where he was making for.
At that speed it could have been anywhere on the planet!
We fished the evening and returned a number of small trout, keeping a brace each that were of a good size, but I have never forgotten the exhibition of power and beauty that Great Northern Diver showed us.

25. Vanishing Tay Trout

When I was a boy in the late fifties the Tay was the most fantastic wild brown trout fishery I have ever seen.
Huge fly hatches would make the river literally boil with feeding trout and grayling. I would constantly have to shake salmon parr and young trout from my flies and I would get pulls from really good trout all the time.
It was amongst this large population of fish I learned to fish dry fly, having plenty of targets to drop my fly supposedly 'delicately' above.
Once, whilst in the boat motoring to the top of the beat and around the island above the hotel, Jimmy and I saw a fish feeding right in next to the shingle on the island in a 'hole' that had been formed by the river and we slowly slipped over until we could see it. It was a wild brown trout of perhaps eight or nine pounds lying there gently taking flies, March Browns and the odd Yellow Sally, as they came floating over it.
Up at the Rock Pool we beached the boat so that Jimmy could tie up new Sprats before we began harling and in the early afternoon heat the hatching flies formed a blizzard around us, so much so that those floating down the river built up against the side of the boat in their thousands and came billowing across us.
I can remember Jimmy constantly blowing them from his hands as he worked and brushing them from his face so he could see what he was doing.
The trout were in a feeding frenzy all over the river.
Little did we know that changing farming methods, hill drainage, acid rain and other factors including man would put an end to such hatches and the trout population too.
There was one factor above all else though that guaranteed the end was nigh for the wild brown trout of the river Tay.
It was a Scotsman's belief that he has the right to fish for brown trout wherever he wants to as all brown trout 'belong' to him and we had many a verbal fight with people who came and fished our beat for trout, most with spinning tackle, who

refused to fish with fly or buy a permit or accept that we had a limit on the permits we issued in order to protect the trout stocks.
On one Sunday afternoon in the early seventies we had no less than forty seven central belt trout fishers on the opposite bank of the one and three quarter mile Dunkeld House Hotel beat.
We decided to check them with the intention of not doing anything more than just asking to see how many trout they might have, even though some were spinning with diving minnows and others were fishing Mepps spoons or upstream worms on fly rods. Most of them showed us what they had caught.
Two of them had more than one hundred trout each.
Six or seven had in the region of fifty trout or more each.
Some twenty had more than ten trout and the rest had less than ten trout.
At the time we checked them we estimated they had killed more than nine hundred trout between them and all the middle beats of the river were similarly full of central belt angling clubs fishing the hell out of the trout population.
Jimmy said to me, "This will never last. No natural fishery can withstand this slaughter. We should bid our great wild Tay brown trout farewell because they are going to become extinct."
They very nearly did. By the end of the seventies we hardly saw a trout on the river and the fly hatches were noticeably far less than they had been, due in part to the advent of acid rain. Then, at the eleventh hour, the law was changed and individual fisheries such as the Tay became able to apply to the Secretary of State for Scotland for a Protection Order to be placed on their fishery to protect the trout stocks, as long as they opened up their waters by issuing permits for trout anglers throughout the Tay watershed.
Spinning for trout would be banned.
The Tay eventually got its Protection Order and very slowly the trout population began to recover, but it will never get back to where it was when I was a boy because the feeding has changed so dramatically.
I don't think any of us will ever see another eight or nine pound wild Tay brownie feeding quietly at the edge of the stream, so sad for those who come after us.

26. Eye Eye

The island just upstream of Dunkeld House holds a myriad of memories for me.
One of them occurred in low September water when David Williams and I fished in the boat with Jimmy and we moored at the tail of the island to fish the narrow stream against the far bank. We were spinning pink and red Devons, the preferred colour of the moment, and before long I hooked a fish.
Having been fishing long lines whilst prawning and shrimping on a lower beat the previous week I had not noticed that a long way back up my line it was frayed and, as the fish took a lengthy run down the river, the line parted.
None of us thought this was an exactly clever thing to have happened, particularly me as I rarely broke with a fish, and then the fish came back up into the pool and jumped out of the water right in front of us and we could see the pink Devon flopping about against the swivel just down the line a few feet from the treble hook that seemed to still be firmly embedded in the fish's mouth.
The stream ran strong in there and I suggested that as there was so much line trailing out behind the fish we should put heavy lures on and attempt to catch hold of it.
This was perhaps not as ridiculous a suggestion as it seemed.
We decided to give it a try and persevered with our heavy lures banging the bottom as the fish again jumped in front of us. After some fifteen minutes of pursuing this somewhat hopeful or hopeless activity I suddenly hooked another fish and played it out. However as it came towards the net and I reeled in the last of my line we came upon a curious sight.
One of the treble hooks of my Devon had gone through the eye of the swivel those few feet down the line from the mouth of the fish that had broken me, which was splashing about next to the boat as it was still very well hooked!
We netted the fish and wondered at the odds against this having happened.
I thought about it for a while and then worked out what I felt might be the only plausible explanation.
The broken line had been trailing out behind the fish in the fast current. My lure had picked up this line, probably fairly close to the fish, and had run up it and met the Devon that had been stopped from sliding further down the line by the very swivel I had hooked and that had been the moment that the point of one of my hooks had gone through the eye of the swivel.
At least that's my theory and I'm sticking to it!

27. The Greatest Schemes

It was January 18th 1975 and at Dunkeld House we had caught nothing since the opening day of the Tay salmon season three days previously.
Jack Morris, David's father, was going to fish and I was going to ghillie as it was one of the handful of times in the 25 years I knew him that Jimmy McLean would be unable to ghillie due to illness.
Jack and I were under pressure to get our first fish of the season because during the opening week it would be sure to feature in the media and bring anglers to the hotel.
Fortunately the day turned out to be a good one weather wise, not a driving, cutting East wind with snow flurries on it thankfully, but cold and crisp with a blue sky overhead, perfect for early year fishing.
We harled our way down the beat, covering every possibility where a springer might rest, but not so much as a kelt or a brown trout hungry from the winter pulled our lures. In the centre of the three rods we were fishing was a big salmon fly rod with a stone on the line for a fish to strike against and out either side of it were two spinning rods, nodding away as their lures danced through the currents.
It was past midday and we had rounded the corner above Telford's bridge at Dunkeld and entered the Girnal pool. Both of us scoured the river down to the bridge for signs of fish moving, but there was nothing. Suddenly the tip of the big fly rod lurched downwards, the stone jumped and Jack bent to pick up the rod, only for the reel to fall straight off it into the bottom of the boat!
Some ghillie!
I was trying to wind one of the two spinning rods in and control the boat, but the fly reel was careering around the space between us as the fish tore line off it and as I bent down to attempt to grab it at the same time as Jack we cracked heads!
I simply had to get the two spinning rods in and out of the way and Jack to his credit did get hold of the fly reel whilst keeping the rod upright, but couldn't keep his grip on it with just one hand, let alone get it back onto the rod.
So away around the bottom of the boat it flew again.
"Jimmy'll murder us if we lose this fish!" Jack was desperate and right.
With the two other rods stowed I grabbed the fly reel, which was now heading towards the other end of the boat as the fish ploughed its way down the middle of the river, and eventually we somehow scrambled it back onto the rod and Jack began to fight the fish.
The long and short of it was that in time we landed a fresh run twelve pounder, so we had done our duty to the 'best' of our ability and consequently achieved the desired publicity and received congratulations from Jimmy, brief though he was about it!
To this day we never told anyone how near our greatest schemes to catch that first fish of the season had come to disaster!

28. Difficult Fish

I caught quite a number of fish during the 1972 season, including multiples of every weight up to my biggest salmon, thirty pounds, and I had some right royal battles with some of them, where they tested me to the full.

But there were two fish of lesser weight, but far greater stature in fighting, that gave me more problems than any of the others.

The first was a twelve pounder on Upper Murthly in the BurnMouth.

I hooked it on fly and it began jumping straightaway and never stopped.

It went crashing across the river, then came crashing back at me as I wound furiously, trying to keep up with it. Then it went upstream, then it went downstream and came out cartwheeling through the air. I was sure it would throw the hook as it kept making fast, surging runs and exploding from the river.

Jimmy MacDonald was in the boat with Williams and Morris some five hundred yards below me and they could see the big splashes exploding all around me, so they made their way back up the river. When they got to me they could hardly

believe the fish was ten or twelve pounds, but to prove that it was it launched itself out of the water right beside the boat. So Jimmy Macdonald came ashore and netted it for me after forty minutes of hard going that I had never been in control of and we looked at the beautiful, short, deep fish that had given me so much trouble.
But it was outdone by an even smaller fish.
On the 16th August 1972 I hooked a fish in the Kings Ford from a number that were passing through in front of the hotel and began to play it from the big shingle bank under the high wall at the front of the hotel. It went absolutely nuts. I had eighteen pound breaking strain line on, but it ran to the other bank and away down the pool towards the Cutty Stone in a blistering run. So I walked down the shingle until I was exactly opposite the hotel. Guests gathered on the lawn above the high wall behind me and I could hear them talking about how great it was to see Mr.Miller land a fish. When it jumped out of the water though I blinked in astonishment at its lack of size, even though there was a communal 'Ooooh !' from behind me.
I got it close and decided I would beach it on the shingle. This I did, but as I went to get hold of it at the last second it turned, thrashed itself back into the river and sped across to the other bank again! There were now some thirty or so people gathered behind me as I thought to myself what a right cobblers I was making of landing it.
I brought it in again and the same thing happened, the fish turning just before I got its head onto the shingle and it careered off across the river again.
The third time was ever so much better though.
Absolutely textbook, I don't think.
This time I got it onto the shingle and waded into the river and got behind it.
Now I had it!
Don't you believe it, our friend was just acting dead as he turned yet again and shot straight between my legs and back out into the river, almost breaking my rod tip as I was forced to ballet dance my way off the line running through my crotch. There were lots of 'Oooohs' and 'Aaaahs' going on above me, but now it was a matter of pride not to lose the fish and this time I played it right out (playing to the gallery?) until it was lying on its side exhausted and I made sure it wasn't acting by giving it a couple of prods with my wading stick before beaching it.
There was great applause above me and I doffed my hat whilst hoping there hadn't been too many cameras that had recorded the occasion as I looked down at the valiant little fish that had given such a terrific account of itself.
It turned out to weigh seven pounds.

29. Rick and the Monster

Rick Knight had managed Butterstone Loch, by Dunkeld since he came to work with me after I started it as a trout fishery in the early 1970's and his expertise turned it into one of Scotland's premiere rainbow trout fisheries.
I first met Rick when I was eighteen and over the years we enjoyed some fine sporting moments together. In October 1984 Rick was going to fish a day or two with me at Dunkeld House, but I had gone down with a bad chest infection and was bed ridden.
So we talked about the water height and where the fish were liable to be and on the 6th October he went round to Green Point on the opposite bank to the hotel and ran into a bunch of fish. He took a 16 pounder, then an 18 pounder and, already delighted with his day, ran into a magnificent big fish that gave him a real battle in this special place from which many of the biggest fish caught on the beat used to come, but Rick did well and eventually landed the most fantastic silvery autumn fish that weighed in at 36 pounds.
That year we fished together in the boat on the final day of the season, the 15th October, and got down below Green Point into the Mouse Trap, where I had seen fish rising out in the deep, slower flowing water. Moored against the left hand bank we fished purple prawns with big weights to take them deep.
Fish in the high teens of pounds came flopping out of the water in front of us making splashy rises as some of them leapt sideways across the stream, showing that they were stopped in there. We fished on, tempting fate by letting the weights above our baits touch bottom first before having them swing towards us. Soon enough Rick caught the bottom. Another prawn would have to be tied up, but could he get his end tackle back? He gave his bait's tenacious grip on the river bed some stick, winding down and yanking the rod hard back, but couldn't clear it. He let line away downstream and yanked away at it as he wound it all the way back up, but his bait remained fixed where it was. Resigned to breaking the line he wound down one last time and hit the rod really hard – only to be hit back as something at the end of his line began to move! It was a fish and it had to be big one to have stayed where it was with all the stick Rick had been giving it!
He began losing line really fast. We needed to get the anchor up and get after it quickly, so I went to the bow only to find that the anchor would not release from the riverbed. I went back to the stern, past the now desperate Rick as his line fast disappeared, started the engine, ran the boat forwards over the anchor and out into the river and the weight of the boat forced the anchor off the bottom. I went forward again and hauled the anchor aboard, returned to the engine, turned the boat and blasted full throttle down the river, following Rick's line.
The fish was now moving through the Girnal, on the top bend above Dunkeld Bridge, sliding down the river all the time and heading over to the right hand bank, but at least Rick had gained a lot of line and although we were not yet in control of the situation, it felt like we were. Suddenly he announced he could feel his line rubbing on rocks. We went straight to where his line entered the water and for a minute or two everything was OK. I knew there were no high rocks there, so the fish must have gone right down onto the riverbed.
Then Rick felt the line rubbing hard amongst rocks and suddenly it parted.

Rick was not exactly pleased with this result, which is as polite as I can put it.
For a fish to behave as this one had done it would have to have been a considerable weight and may well have been a monster autumn cock fish as most of them tend to slide down the river after being hooked.
It was certainly the biggest fish Rick had ever had hold of.
How big?
We'll never know.

30. Hartley Byrom's Big Fish

I was at school with Hartley Byrom but didn't know him well there and then found he was to be a fishing guest at Dunkeld House from our very first year in 1969.
He was a nice chap, a gentleman, always polite and friendly and he loved to fish in the boat with Jimmy.
During the afternoon of the penultimate day of the 1971 season, the 14th October, Jimmy, David Morris and I were out in the boat and we harled down past Hartley, who was fishing from the bank in the Grotto, and exchanged a few words with him. Then we harled on down through the Gage and Fifey pools into the Cathedral Stream and on into the Sandy Pool above Dunkeld Bridge. We were blethering away to each other when Jimmy asked if we could see something a long way up above us on the bank in the Gage Tree pool. We looked and could just make out a small white thing going up and down. For a second or two we wondered what it was and then realised it could be Hartley trying to attract our attention. So we reeled our rods in and set off up the river.
As we got to the tail of the Gage, out of the strong Cathedral Stream, I could see Hartley's rod was bent well over and he began waving us off towards the other bank. We gave him a wide berth and came in to the bank above him.
"This is a pig!" he exclaimed, apparently having seen the fish roll over after it took his Toby spoon. "I put new 12 pound line on, but I can't do a thing with it."
Jimmy and I gave each other a knowing look.
In big water in late autumn on the Tay, with forty pound class fish going about, neither of us would fish anything less than eighteen pound breaking strain. You had to be able to fight a really big fish on some kind of terms otherwise you were unlikely to land it. We took Hartley into the boat and moved out into the middle of the river next to the fish. I went up to the bow, shielded the glare from the water and looked down into the depths. There, not far below me, was a big, grey, Nautilus submarine shape that seemed to be hanging effortlessly in the current.
We stayed like that for some twenty minutes with nothing happening and the light beginning to fail as evening came on. I said I thought I could stick the gaff in the fish, but that we may well lose it. We decided to give it a try with Hartley putting maximum pressure on and so down to the fish I went with the long handled fixed gaff. As the gaff touched the fish it exploded from the pool down into the Cathedral Stream in a split second, Hartley's line hissing through the water and as it went another massive fish, big and silver, leapt high into the air to get out of the way of it. It was a fish in the mid-thirties and it landed on its side with a heck of a splash.

We got down to Hartley's fish and the lights on the bridge came on, soon it would be completely dark. We slipped in behind the lower Cathedral railings and tied the boat up with Hartley fighting the fish from there.
In fifteen minutes he got it some five yards closer and then it went back to its original position and began slipping down the river, nearer to the bridge.
It would be a fairly brave man who would follow a fish through Dunkeld bridge into the rapids either side of the island immediately below it, even in big water. We never did it and lost very few fish through the bridge, but we were certainly not going to try it now that it was dark.
Jimmy's son, David, turned up and I remember there being several of us on the bank. Hartley got out of the boat and walked down to get opposite the fish. Jimmy and I exchanged a quiet word that we may well lose it through the bridge, but that I would take the gaff and get as far out in the river as possible in case we got the hint of a chance.
At one stage Jimmy asked Hartley if he was really putting the fish under pressure and passed his big, rough thumb across the taught line coming from the reel, producing a high pitched 'Ting'!
Yes, he had all the pressure on it he could muster without breaking the line!
In the darkness I was in the river up to my chest without waders on and those on the bank were looking along the line in the lights from the bridge, trying to guide me to the fish, when it suddenly slipped down right under the nearest arch of the bridge into the really fast water.
We were about to lose it.
Then everyone behind me shouted that it was between me and them!
I turned and could just see a big, black back and dorsal fin sailing past me, stuck the gaff into it and made for the bank.
Once there the others hauled the fish out and dispatched it.
Hartley was ecstatic as the odds had been against him all the way.
The fish, having been tired, must have felt the strong stream under the bridge and, not wanting to go into it, had come back up into the tail of the Sandy.
It weighed thirty six pounds and took Hartley Byrom over an hour and a half to land.

31. Jack Charlton

A film crew appeared at the hotel one day wanting to make a salmon fishing film with Jack Charlton, the ex-England footballer.
The programme (and book) were to be called 'Go Fishing'.
But they had turned up with the river in flood, dirty and almost a foot and a half above big fishing height.
We agreed they would shoot some footage of Jack and I on the bank and would come back in the autumn to shoot Jack fighting a salmon.
So we went up and down the riverbank filming all kinds of stuff.
Down in the Girnal pool, as you come into sight of Dunkeld bridge, there is a big water lie on the inside of the bend on the left hand bank. Fish that run from way below the bridge battle their way through the rapids and then the Cathedral Stream, which is really strong when the river is high and on up through the Gage Tree and Grotto into the Girnal and then they draw into this quieter patch of water that is tucked inside the bend of the river, with the strong stream flowing on the outside of it.
Bored with filming I walked up to this supposed 'hot spot' and launched a big Toby Salmo spoon with an ounce and a half of lead up the line from it no more than fifteen yards out into the stream.
Letting it sink I tightened up on the lure so I could feel it working its way across the current and let it swing round. The fish took it about sixth cast and I yelled for Jack and the film crew to come up to me.
I should have known there would be a problem earlier on when Jack produced a closed face trout reel with eight pound breaking strain line on it to fish for salmon with and promptly lost one of my best Norwegian spoons on the bottom.
We agreed that Jack would say into camera that he had hooked the fish with his first cast with my rod, but since then almost everyone I have ever met who saw the video or TV programme says they immediately realised I had hooked the fish and handed him the rod!
Jack proceeded to stand there and wind and wind my Ambassadeur reel so that it made a continuous clicking noise because he was not gaining line, the clutch on the reel was making the clicking that told everyone this story. I advised him to 'wind down the line' put his thumb on the drum of the reel and 'pump' the fish, i.e. draw the fish towards him under pressure, then wind down the line again, jam his thumb on the drum and draw the fish towards him again.
He took no notice and stood there winding and winding and the reel kept on clicking and clicking.
This was a disaster. Any angler would know Jack was not fighting the fish properly and I said so to the director. Time and again I asked Jack to stop winding and pump the fish, explaining what he should do and how to do it.
Time and again he took no notice.
In desperation I asked the director what I should do. Could they cut out any bits of me shouting at Jack Charlton?
Yes, said the director, go ahead. He wanted it to be right.
"Jack! Will you stop winding that bloody reel!" Charlton looked at me a little surprised.

"Put your bloody thumb on the bloody drum and pump the bloody fish like I've been bloody well telling you to!"
With that Jack Charlton began to play the fish properly. It was a great relief.
Now I had another problem. Not having expected to hook a fish in such conditions I had nothing with me to land it with. No net, no gaff. The fish came into the bank not fully played out and I attempted to 'tail' it out, grab it just above the tail and lift it onto the bank. Of course I failed, the fish being too strong for me, and away it went back out into the stream. All caught on camera.
Later the fishing correspondent of one of the Glasgow newspapers would tear into me for showing young anglers the wrong way to go about landing a salmon!
The second time it came in though tail it I did and put a lovely nineteen pounder on the bank.
Success!
The film was made, the television programme, video and book would come out, everyone was happy, the director was delirious and Jack promised me a couple of football Cup Final tickets in celebration.
I never heard from him again.

32. The Wader-less Fisherman

We had a poacher on the Tay who used to poach with rod and line, but wore no waders as he fished.
Instead he would wear the bottom half of a wet suit and flippers!
His top half above the water would appear perfectly normally clothed.
If he was about to be caught he would quickly put on goggles and snorkel, abandon his rod into the river, swim out into the current and disappear downstream covering quite long distances under water.
Sometimes he would go for miles, making it very difficult for those chasing him to work out exactly where he was going to come out and he had obviously chosen clever places to exit the river where it would be difficult to see him, perhaps with heavy woodland cover right down to the water.
Presumably he either had a motorbike stashed somewhere downstream or he dried himself off and walked home or hitched a lift to somewhere.
He was never caught and was undoubtedly guilty of poaching many fish from the Tay until finally, after trying to make another of his wader-less escapes one day, he was never seen or heard of again.

33. The Bet

John Shepherd and his pal Derek Towers fished quite a bit at Dunkeld House over the years and I found them both to have a tremendous sense of humour.
On one occasion Jaguar were having a launch of their latest model at the hotel and were staying with us whilst motoring journalists photographed and test drove their cars. They were always in the bar and the managing director got friendly with John and Derek, who one evening made a bet with him.
The main drive to Dunkeld House was almost a mile long before it reached the A9. If you then turned left, instead of right into the village of Dunkeld, and you headed up the A9 for about three quarters of a mile you came upon our back drive, which began at Polney Lodge where Jimmy McLean lived.
Shepherd drove a long wheel base diesel Land Rover and he challenged the Jaguar boys to a race down the main drive, up the A9 and down the back drive back to the hotel car park. Of course they were keen to take him on, but Shepherd said they would have to be handicapped as his diesel took a little time to pre-heat the fuel before he could start it.
So it was agreed they would have to drink a pint of water before being able to start and this would give him time to get to his vehicle and get it going. They agreed, but to make it more interesting Shepherd made the bet for ownership of the managing director's fabulous sheepskin lined overcoat.
There was a bit of deliberation over this before the managing director decided he would take John Shepherd's bet.
The start would be made from the hotel bar and everyone prepared themselves.
Someone shouted 'Go!'
John Shepherd put a pint of boiling water on the bar, walked outside, got into his vehicle, drove round the course, drove back into the car park, got out and walked into the bar and the managing director was still sitting there waiting for the pint of water to cool down!
John wore the lovely coat for a couple of days before he gave it back!

34. The Call of Nature

David Morris began his salmon fishing career on Scotland's river Tay in 1969.
He and his father Jack were friends of my family and David had been at the same school in Lancashire that I went to.
Having a tremendous sense of humour and being a keen sportsman made him a natural at salmon fishing and he took to it like a duck to water.
He fished with Jimmy McLean at Dunkeld House and Jimmy MacDonald down at Murthly but it was a while before he got his first fish.
In fact the very first one he got hold of was on Upper Murthly and of some size, in the high twenties, but it snagged him up on a previously unknown dead tree that must have arrived during recent winter floods. David was distraught and I felt for him as Jimmy MacDonald told me it had been a good one.
So I gave him the best of the boat one early March week in 1971 on Murthly and on the Thursday, with him still not having caught his first fish, our turn came to fish the Lower beat. In the afternoon I decided to keep the two of them company, so we set off harling up above Miss Ballantyne's Boat pool (well surely it will always belong to Miss Ballantyne as she caught Britain's record 64lb. salmon in it?).
The day was grey and extremely cold with a biting Easterly wind blowing straight up the river into our faces as we sat there looking at Jimmy whilst scouring the river below for signs of fish. We got down to the Boat pool and harled the Bargee Stone at the head, after which Jimmy carefully searched every nook and cranny for a fresh run fish. The wind became stronger and stronger, blowing in straight from Murmansk it seemed and the day grew ominously dark. Still we cracked jokes and told stories and enjoyed the pleasure of being in a boat on a great Tay salmon beat together.
As we neared Caputh bridge Jimmy's eyes caught mine and he looked over to our bank, signalling the question of whether we should perhaps call it a day. Despite the temperature falling steadily I knew how desperate David was to get his first fish, so with the slightest of movement I barely shook my head and we continued on through the bridge down into Sparriemuir.
Our faces were turning blue from the cold. At least David's and mine were because Jimmy was sitting there with his back to the weather and the hood of his jacket up over his hat, affording him some protection. I have never minded the cold and love to fish all weathers, appreciating the fact that the extremes are a constant a reminder of the slender thread my existence hangs by, promptly followed by my enormous appreciation of the warmth of the log fires we used to run in the hall lounge at Dunkeld House during the winters!
But it really was bitter cold, cutting into us like a knife. We had been fishing for three hours or more, the light was failing and the jokes and stories were getting less as the cold penetrated right through us.
Again Jimmy's eyes asked the question, again I declined and knew he understood the reason as I kept turning my eyes to David.
And then at last David's rod jerked and bent as a fish came on. He grabbed it and tried to wind and gain line, but he was now so numb with cold that even trying to crank the handle of the reel was extremely difficult.
Still as we made for the shore he was doing his very best, as was the fish.

Once sorted out and tied to the river bank Jimmy offered him the odd word of advice and told him how well he was doing. The sheer desperation of getting the fish in to see whether it was a kelt or a salmon was tempered by David's shaking from the cold and the difficulty he was having in winding the reel. Gradually though he came on terms with the fish and after a few short runs close to the boat the fish came up, turned on its side and Jimmy netted it.
"Is it a fish or a kelt?" asked David with trepidation in his voice.
"It's a fish!" I replied, looking at the fine fourteen pound springer that Jimmy was knocking on the head.
I slapped David on the back a few times and shook him by the shoulders.
"Congratulations, mate! Most people would have turned it in ages ago in this cold."
"I had to stay out here, I had to, just in case. I've never been so bloody cold in my life!" replied an ecstatic Morris.
He was as proud of his first salmon as an angler could be.
Jimmy had washed the fish off and placed it between him and the two of us in the bottom of the boat so that David could continue his appreciation of it. Then he looked up and, with a twinkle in his eye, said the sentence that David and I will never forget,
"Well, I'm really glad you got that one David, I was needing a pee!"

35. First Name Basis

Driving across Caputh bridge one lunchtime I spied Jimmy MacDonald bringing his party of anglers to the bank in front of Miss Ballantyne's house, so I went down to say hello.
Jimmy had picked up his fishers from the opposite bank and was now helping all four anglers ashore and handing them their bags and tackle.
There was one tall, gangly man, bedecked in yellow tweed, who turned back as the party had walked to the lunch hut and shouted,
"Ghillie! We'll see you back at two o'clock then?" I cringed at his use of the title 'ghillie' instead of addressing Jimmy MacDonald as 'Jimmy'.
Surely he could remember a ghillie's first name?
I walked up and Jimmy and I chatted about the fishing and what was going on at Murthly and Dunkeld House.
Suddenly there came this shout again from the yellow bedecked one,
"Ghillie! Ghillie! Come here will you, ghillie! We want to take a picture!"
We continued talking, both of us ignoring his extreme rudeness that I don't think either of us could quite believe.
"Ghillie! Are you coming?" came the shout again.
"I better go, Jess."
"Yes Jimmy, before I go over there and give that idiot a lesson in manners."
"I was beginning to think of doing that myself," said Jimmy as we parted.
I have often pondered whether that afternoon Jimmy might have taken the tweed bedecked one to fish some special part of the river where the last fish had been caught in 1867.....

36. Miss Ballantyne and The Ministers

Miss Georgina Ballantyne, who landed the 64lb. British Record Salmon in 1922, was a kindly soul. Though slight of stature and suffering badly from arthritis she was such a pleasure to talk to and her wonderful, sparkling eyes and highland charm fronted an exceptional knowledge of the Lower Murthly beat where she lived, right on the famous Boat pool in which she had caught the great fish.

We used to chat across the little gate on the river side of her house whenever I was fishing there. If you stop on Caputh bridge and look upstream hers was the house on the right hand bank next to the bridge and if you look on up the Boat Pool you will see the big Bargee stone over to the left at the head of the pool, next to which in 1922 she hooked the sixty four pounder that made her world famous.

One morning I was down there early sorting my tackle out when she hailed me from the wicker gate at the front of her garden.

"Mr.Miller, there was a big run of fish came into the Boat pool after you left last night. There were a lot of them and they stopped overnight and were splashing about everywhere. Bars of silver they were, but they took off about half an hour ago, if you're in luck you'll be sure to find the tail enders up around the corner in the Ministers."

I thanked her for this invaluable tip and hastened my preparations. Shortly my party arrived and, even though I was the host, immediately laid claim to the supposedly 'best' places on the beat. Two would fish the Boat pool from either bank, one would go up to the Firs on the opposite bank below the Ministers and another would go in the boat with ghillie Jimmy MacDonald.

"Oh well," I sighed resignedly, "I guess I'll just have to take a walk up and fish the Ministers then."

I could sense their pleasure in having managed to 'relegate' me to the Ministers, out of which we had not caught a fish that week, whilst they had succeeded in securing the 'best' of the beat for themselves.

I hurried along the bank and as I was getting close to the pool I saw three fish rise one after another, two were head and tailing runners, travelling on through, but one was stopped I was sure.

I threw out a black and gold Penney Devon and a fish grabbed it first cast.

I had three one after another, but then the run was through and gone and I touched nothing else.

The three of them were covered in sea lice and had the shimmering colours of the Atlantic on their flanks, they were the very finest of spring fish.

When I carried them back at lunchtime I found to my astonishment that the rest of my party had caught nothing.

Georgina Ballantyne, as usual, had been absolutely right.

Williams, Morris and Miller

37. Lord Sandwich

David Williams, David Morris and myself fished together a minimum of twice a year for many years and we generated an extreme amount of humour and leg pulling when together, which goes hand in glove with fishing.
One day we were down at Murthly and Jimmy MacDonald had gone home for his lunch. We were starving hungry having been out from early morning and unpacked the lunch that had been prepared for us at the hotel.
There was nothing to drink. No beers, no flasks of soup or coffee, nothing.
So we discussed the situation and eventually had a mock argument about which of us should go back and pick up our liquid refreshment.
Williams and I ganged up on Morris, but it took a lot of pressure to get him to agree to go back, his biggest concern seemed to be that we would eat his sandwiches whilst he was gone.
We told him not to be so childish and stopped him from taking any sandwiches with him under our guarantee we would not touch our own sandwiches until he got back, when all three of us could enjoy our lunch together.
This mock argument went on for a bit and Williams and I had to swear on the Bible that we wouldn't eat Morris's sandwiches and eventually he drove off to go and get the drinks.
We waited and talked about the fish and how things were set for the afternoon.
We waited and talked about possibly fishing together down south in England.

We waited and talked about putting the world to rights.
We waited and waited, but no David Morris appeared.
After almost an hour it was time for Jimmy MacDonald to come back so we could resume fishing.
We had to have something to eat.
We came to the conclusion that Morris had gone into the hotel dining room and got himself a slap up lunch. So we unpacked the sandwiches, unwrapped them and were just about to take our first bite when Morris suddenly jumped out from behind a bush and shouted,
"I knew you'd eat my bloody sandwiches!"

38. The Japs and the Dam Fish

David Williams, David Morris and I once fished a spring week on Murthly and each of us caught fish except Morris.
When I say we had a week we had five days on Murthly, which was all the estate could give us, and then the Saturday at the dam at Pitlochry. As the first five days wore on Morris became more and more desperate to catch a fish, but to no avail. Despite fishing long and hard he never got so much as a pull.
At the end of our spell we said our goodbyes to Jimmy MacDonald knowing that Morris had just one more day to catch a fish that spring.
So it was Saturday 26th April 1974 when we took up our stations on either bank of the stretch of the Tummel below the dam, David Williams and I on the right hand bank and David Morris opposite us (and therefore on the left hand bank!).
As the morning wore on Morris began making Japanese noises at Williams.
Kung Fu was all the rage and so we assumed Morris was up to his normal antics and was winding Williams up.
A loud 'Aah.....So!' came across the river at us, followed by short, guttural noises that Japanese martial arts fighters might make. Williams asked me what the heck Morris was up to and I had to declare I had no idea as the intonations from the land of the rising sun continued to float across the water to us.
After a while Williams looked over his shoulder to find about forty Japanese tourists standing immediately behind him, watching him fish!
How long they had been there we didn't know, but Morris had been making those noises for a heck of a long time!
Just before lunch Morris finally hooked a fish that gave him some real stick and ran up the river as if it was trying to enter the fish ladder and get through the dam! Fortunately he managed to turn it and back down the river it came. The neck of the river there is not very wide so we could easily converse with each other and Williams and I encouraged Morris to stop messing about and get the fish in, whilst he battled away.
Then his line parted!
It's a rocky, ledgy kind of place up at the dam and lines easily become frayed and fish kiss you goodbye. Morris slapped his rod point down into the water in disgust. We felt for him as that was the only fish hooked so far and it looked possible that we might not get another.

After a while of our commiserating across the water he began to reel in his broken line and we prepared to commence fishing again.
But as he reeled in his line suddenly tightened and Morris astonishingly found he had the fish on again!
We were as amazed as he was. He proceeded to fight and land the fish, which turned out to be a fine looking 22 pounder.
Before long we worked out what had happened.
When the fish had come back down the river from the entrance to the fish ladder up above it had snagged the line around a rock in midstream and for a while David had been fighting it with the line running around the rock and the fish downstream of it, which none of us had realised.
Then the line had flipped off the top of the rock, creating the impression it had broken and the fish was gone, but as he had reeled in the slack Morris had come back into contact with the fish once more and had consequently broken his duck for the week.
He was a greatly relieved man, I can tell you!

39. Not Big Enough

One April in the early 1970's Williams, Morris and I were fishing the Lower Murthly Beat of the Tay. We had caught one fish for the day and I was just finishing off in the evening sunshine, fishing the fly down the right hand bank of the Boat Pool, opposite Georgina Ballantyne's house.
Quite a big fish kept on making a splashy rise at the boil above Caputh bridge, but nothing happened on my run down. Williams and Morris came and sat on the bank and, having seen the fish rise two or three times, urged me to run down the bottom half of the pool again. This time when the fly came to the boil there was an almighty 'take' and battle commenced.
As I fought the fish a car drew up on the bridge just above us and out of it got two men dressed in suits.
They could well have been a salesman and his area manager.
Eventually the fish came in and looked to be twenty pounds or so.
As it lay in the rocks at the side of the water and David Morris was about to deliver the 'coup de grace' it dawned on me that we had a problem and I stopped him just in time.
"It's a kelt, lads."
They looked at me in disbelief. I must admit any angler who had taken that fish home could not have been blamed for doing so. It looked perfect in every respect and only if you had been used to seeing this particular strain of spent fish would you recognise it.
Luckily I had been taught by those who had experience of these fresh salmon lookalikes and who used to call them 'Loch Tay' kelts.
The two Davids closely examined the fish and distinct doubt appeared in their minds as to whether it actually was a fresh run salmon. But the down turned eye, maggots in the gills, pointed teeth, black topped fins, half open vent, along with the

slight slimness not normally associated with a fresh run fish was enough to convince them and David Morris turned to return it to the water.
As the two men on the bridge looked on aghast the large silver fish was returned to the Tay and sped away. David washed his hands in the river, looked up at the two of them on the bridge and shouted,
"Not big enough!"
We've always imagined them going into a pub somewhere that evening and proclaiming that a bunch of anglers they had witnessed putting a massive salmon back into the Tay to be completely and utterly mad!

40. My Wanger!

Colonel Peter Castle Smith lives down on the Murthly beat and is one of the great legendary salmon fly fishers. Also a great wader, aided by his height, he has fished the two Murthly beats for more than thirty five years and has seen ghillies come and go. We have always got on famously and Peter once tied me his three favourite salmon fly patterns, a Munro Killer, a Prawn Fly and a Silver Stoats Tail, each in a whole range of sizes on treble hooks except for the very small sizes that were tied on doubles. For maybe twenty years I never bothered using any other flies wherever I fished in the UK and, on their day, they were as deadly as anything else being used.
In fact there were many days when the fly did better than anything.
Right from when I met him around 1970 Peter told me to have more faith in the fly and not in what he called my 'wanger', meaning my spinning rod, so called because with a spinning rod you 'wang' the bait out across the river when you cast, at least according to Peter that is.
So I began to fish the fly more and the more I fished it the more I caught and the more faith I gained in fishing it, having soon taken fish on fly in all kinds of river conditions from low water drought to full, dirty flood.
Whenever I was fishing on Murthly Peter would enquire whether I was going to be using my 'wanger' with a disapproving tone and so gradually my 'wanger' was relegated to second class and the fly became my premium method of fishing.
Harry & Irene Swanson lived in Reno, Nevada in the USA and I had met Harry in the States in the early seventies when he very kindly got me onto British Columbia's Dean River at Robbie Scott's camp for a week as his guest.
He wanted to catch an Atlantic Salmon in Scotland and so in the early 1970's he and Irene came to fish Murthly with me during one April that proved to be very good.
There was Morris, Williams, Harry & Irene Swanson, Peter Castle Smith and me with ghillie Jimmy MacDonald and a riotous week it turned out to be.
On the first morning Harry was fishing his single handed fly rod on Miss Ballantyne's bank of the Boat pool and we both saw a fish head and tail as it came through Caputh bridge. There is a pipe that runs out into the river, disappearing into the river bed just above the bridge and at that height I warned Harry the fish may well pull around in front of the pipe and he should cover it. The fish promptly

took him and Harry Swanson landed his first Atlantic Salmon, a lovely ten pounder.
At lunchtime the party gathered and Peter, seeing I also had a fish, enquired whether I had got it using my 'wanger'. Irene went bright red and asked Harry, who had a smile on his face, whether she had heard correctly. As Peter went on about how he didn't agree with me using my 'wanger' and that his opinion was that my 'wanger' should be banned from the river, Irene collapsed in hysterics.
What we didn't understand, as Peter continued to berate the use of my 'wanger', is that in the United States your 'wang' is your private part.
The more Peter went on the more Harry and Irene became hysterical. Finally they explained what it was Peter was saying they found so hilarious and from then on the word 'wanger' was used at every available opportunity by the Brits in the party.
Peter and I used seventeen and half foot Bruce & Walker carbon fibre salmon fly rods, but Harry's single handed Steelhead fly rod became referred to as a 'toothpick' by Peter. However I remember Harry catching just as many fish with his toothpick as the two of us did with our long rods.
We ran into a big run of April fish and Irene took a formidable thirty pounder from the boat up in the Firs that took forty minutes of hard going to land.
They were all magnificent, hard fighting fish and the week was both wonderful in fishing terms as well as being enormously funny.

41. Kowalski

Back in the mid-1970's I met Richard C. 'Dick' Dryer.
I was out on a skerry (a reef) trying to flight ducks in the Orkney Islands to the north of Scotland when he came crawling around the corner of the skerry and greeted me. I'd had no idea he was there.
He turned out to be an extraordinarily infuriating American with whom anyone could get angry in an instant and in later years there were times when I could wilfully have killed him, but those stories I'll leave for a later time.
Anyway here we were up at Balfour Castle on the Island of Shapinsay, the home of Captain and Mrs. Ted Zawadski, whose son Richard had invited me up to shoot the difficult wild duck that came so fast on the Orkney winds.
I am in danger of digressing so let's get back to a fishing story.
One evening we were some fifteen or so people having dinner together when Dick Dryer proceeded to tell the following story:
"Over in America scientists have been researching for years and have finally developed a new breed of fish that is crossbred from three species, the Coho Salmon, the Walleye Pike and the Muskie (Muskelunge, for all intents and purposes another North American Pike).
It's an incredible fish that goes to the sea to feed and comes back to the rivers to spawn and kills anything that gets in its way."
We were enthralled with the development of such a fish and then Dryer said the words that began the slide his life would be on from that moment, at least as far as the Zawadski's were concerned.
"So as the fish is a cross between the Coho, the Walleye and the Muskie we called it the Kowalski!"
We were in a Polish household and there was a stunned silence for a moment or two, but before anyone could say anything Dryer administered his 'coup de grace'.
"But of course," he said, beaming at his host, "we had to teach it to swim!"
With that he proceeded to roar with laughter and I began to wish I wasn't there.
It was so embarrassing I can't put it into words.
After dinner I asked Dryer what on earth he thought he'd been playing at.
"Listen, two years ago Zawadski told a joke against us Americans and I've been waiting to pay him back ever since!"
Well payback time it might have been, but things never quite got back on the same footing with Captain Ted after that.

On The Glass

42. Willie the Fish

I used to go up to the River Glass and fish it with Alan Allison (Loch Leven), staying at Murdo Mackenzie's Glen Affric hotel at Cannich.
Murdo was well known as was ghillie Donald McClennan, nicknamed Blue Charm, who lived across from the hotel.
I once had a fifteen minute phone conversation with a man from British Telecom's directory enquiries about Murdo when enquiring for the number of the hotel so well known was he.
There was also an ex-ghillie up there known as 'Willie the Fish'.
The Glass falls into the river Beauly on which Lord Lovatt owns a large stretch and which in turn falls into the Beauly Firth just north of Inverness.
There are two Borland salmon lifts on the Glass, which are fish lifts that let salmon in and then lift them to the top of a dam and let them out to continue their journey. It's all very civilised and free to the salmon.
The Beauly was fishing well, but the fish weren't yet in the Glass, much to our disdain. We fished away, but it seemed that we were fishing empty water. Around day three of our week a curious story circulated the locality.
Concerned at the lack of fish in the Glass the Fisheries Superintendent and his assistant had gone to visit the two Borland lifts to check they were working properly.
At that time both lifts were being operated by Willie the Fish.
All seemed OK at the first lift, but when they arrived at the second they were just in time to find Willie the Fish packing the last of dozens of salmon into his car and apprehended him. How many salmon he had taken over that period we do not

know but on the very first lift after he had been relieved of his job a record number of over six hundred salmon were lifted!
We listened with amazement to the story of Willie the Fish's brazened thievery and went out on the empty river the next day with our hopes high, but it remained empty until around two o'clock in the afternoon when a veritable wall of salmon, filling the river from bank to bank, came past us moving together up the empty river. So we gave them a wave and doffed our hats in salute.
The fishing wasn't very good for the remainder of the week though as the fish, held up for far too long below the Borland lifts, raced on past us.

43. Dog Fly Days

The Highland rivers above Inverness are truly joyous to behold as they run through the most wonderful Scottish scenery, the river Glass being no exception. Alan and I used to enjoy a week's fly fishing on the Glass and although we never scored heavily our appreciation of every fish we caught was huge.
Alan would take two or three of his black Labrador bitches along, who were never any trouble and would sit quietly at the riverside.
I was once wading, fly fishing out in the stream and decided to return to our 'base' on the riverbank to get a cup of tea. Alan was upstream somewhere, out of sight. The wind was blowing and, as I turned and looked back to where our gear was lying, I saw one of his dogs lift her head, above which I also suddenly saw a salmon fly, hanging from a dropper on one of the spare rods, swinging back and forth in the wind.
As I walked towards her, not in my wildest dreams thinking anything untoward was going to happen, the dog raised its head and snapped at the fly and I saw the fly cast tighten. I immediately yelled just as loud as I could my full sergeant-major command for total and absolute doggy obedience that threatened death and destruction if it wasn't obeyed.
I had used it with great success on my own dog Jake from time to time in emergencies, until he got used to it, after which he would simply give me looks that were his version of our own two fingered salute. Fortunately the bitch froze and I reached her still bellowing my most frightening deep power commands.
She never moved a muscle as I knelt beside her.
"There's a good dog, now don't you go moving, just hold steady, there's a good girl," I cradled her head in my hands and found to my utter astonishment that the double hooked Hairy Mary was not hooked into her mouth, it was stuck right up her nose!
It was lying completely inside one nostril, how it got in there was a miracle in itself, but the real wonder was that the hooks had not been driven in, however any movement from the dog would be fatal. As I talked in soothing tones to keep her calm she still did not move, seeming to understand that I was trying to help.
Ever so gently and carefully I teased the fly forwards in her nostril so as not to jag her with the points of the hooks and gradually I was able to ease it right out and clip it up on to a rod ring.
I then petted the dog and made a bit of a fuss of her and she seemed happy.

Quite how she would have played on a fourteen foot spliced Sharpes of Aberdeen impregnated cane salmon fly rod has been a question I have mulled over ever since.
A while later I was sitting next to his dogs enjoying my tea when Alan appeared and I told him the story. He looked at me with incredulity and I became slightly annoyed, thinking he didn't believe me.
"You mean the old bitch? That one over there?"
"Yes."
"You're joking, surely?"
"No, Alan, I'm not joking, that's what happened, just as I told you."
He could tell I was a bit miffed at not being believed.
"It's not that I don't believe you about the fly it's just that I find it hard to believe about that dog."
"Why?"
"Well you try and go near her now."
I was puzzled, so I took a couple of paces over towards the old bitch and extended my hand to pet her. She nearly took my hand off, snapping viciously, snarling loudly with lips curled back showing her fangs and her hackles went up. I could not get near her.
"See what I mean? And she held still for you? That was a miracle."
There seemed to have been a lot of miracles going on that afternoon, but it had all been down to the dog's immediate understanding that she had a problem and I had been trying to help her.
After which she promptly reverted to her apparently nasty self!

44. Bill Met By Moonlight

Sea trout fishing is addictive.

Out in the middle of the night casting your fly or flies into the darkness never knowing from one second to the next whether one of the greatest game fish in Britain will spot your small fly and come hurtling out of the depths to smash take it.
The rod can just about be wrenched from your hands, especially if you've been fishing for two or three hours with nothing happening and you've stopped paying proper attention, which is typical of a sea trout take.
There was a guy called Bill I used to fish sea trout with and we did a bit of wheeling and dealing together, especially with vintage fishing tackle, which I used to collect.
We'd had a few sea trout escapades together and once he had dropped a valuable old fishing reel into the hotel for me to take a look at. I had been impressed, it was worth hundreds of Pounds. The next day in the afternoon he called me, I told him what it was worth and he said he was going to a big car boot sale early the next morning and he needed the money to take with him in case there was something expensive there he should buy.
But he couldn't get to me until late in the evening so we arranged to meet up at 10.00pm. at Kinkell Bridge on the river Earn and fish for sea trout through midnight. I got there early, tackled up and walked to the top of the beat to begin fishing and soon caught and returned a Whitling, a young sea trout of about half a pound. Engrossed in my fishing I realised that time must be wearing on as it was dark and indeed it had gone 11.00pm., but where was Bill?
Remember this was in the days long before mobile phones!
It was a velvet dark night as I fished stealthily down the beat, not wishing to disturb any possible large sea trout that was considering attacking my fly.
No sign of Bill anywhere though and now it was around 12.30a.m.
Suddenly and unusually the moon came out as the cloud broke away and lit everything up.
I couldn't see anyone down the river below me, but got the fright of my life when I turned and there was Bill standing right next to me!
He had started at the top of the beat and waded down behind me, he knew I was there because he'd heard the clicking of the clutch on my reel as I pulled line from the drum and he'd just kept steadily fishing down as I had been doing below him.
Except he had deliberately kept silent!
So as soon as my heart had calmed down and I had stopped berating him for frightening the life out of me, I paid Bill's bill to him out there in the river.
By moonlight.

45. Helmsdale Hiatus

Captain Ted Zawadski used to very kindly invite me to fish the phenomenal river Helmsdale during April.

That far north though April showers could be pretty ferocious.

We used to fish big, weighted Waddingtons (flies tied with a long body and a fixed treble hook at the end) and the Helmsdale spring fish we used to catch were absolutely magnificent.

One lovely bright, sunny day snowstorms kept coming at us with bright sunlight of half an hour to an hour or so in between them. We could see them building higher up the valley and then they would suddenly be upon us. Some of them were pretty horrendous with high winds and blizzard conditions until they passed. We would retire and lie in the heather until a bad storm was through, but as I only fished the Helmsdale once a year I found this very frustrating.

Finally, in the middle of one long storm, my patience ran out and I got up, worked out my line and somehow cast it across the river in the howling wind and a fish took my Waddington immediately. We got it in with the snow going sideways and then the sun came out and everyone began fishing again.

A while later another big snowstorm appeared and so we retired once more to the heather, but Captain Ted decided he was going to have a go at seeing if he could emulate my performance. He stood there in the wind with heavy snow swirling around him, worked his line out and prepared to make a powerful cast to launch his Waddington across the river.

Back came the rod, the line went out behind him and then, just at the moment he put all his effort into launching the thing, a devastating blast of wind hit us.
Forwards went the rod, but the line was not where it was supposed to be.
The Waddington, now travelling at a million miles a second, proceeded to strike Captain Ted full square on the back of his head with a resounding 'thwack!'.
Fortunately he was wearing a hat.
Unfortunately this was now carried across the Helmsdale and proceeded to land delicately on the other bank. For a second or two both we and Ted hesitated as the middle of his line touched the river and then his hat was jerked from the other bank into the freezing river water and he had to ignominiously reel it back across the Helmsdale to a huge round of applause from those of us lying in the heather.
He took it all in good part.

46. There Goes The Neighbourhood

The next day would be my birthday, the 26th April 1972, and the fishing prospects were the greatest I ever witnessed on Lower Murthly or indeed in my entire salmon fishing career.
It was already a good week, we had caught a number of fresh run springers, but all day on the 25th fish had been pouring through under Caputh bridge into the Boat pool. I had been watching them along with ghillie Jimmy MacDonald.
We had talked about what was going on at lunchtime, but throughout the afternoon still they kept coming, some running on through, but most of them seemed to be stopping.
As we stood by the cars after my party had left I was talking with Jimmy when suddenly there were dozens of fish in the air at the same time all over the Boat pool. We stood and watched as a hundred fish or more, bars of silver, rose one after another for ten minutes or so.
"Jess, you've got to get down here at first light tomorrow. These fish are stopped and we'll do very well. It could be a record spring day. I can't remember ever seeing it like this."
I went home and prepared to take Jimmy's advice by sorting out my tackle, re-tying knots and making sure everything was ready. I was up well before the light, made some soup and sandwiches for lunch and took off down to Murthly.
But even as I drove onto the river bank I sensed that something was wrong.
I could feel it as I glanced at the river in the half light. I took my rods from the roof of the vehicle and began to walk up to the head of the Boat pool.
What on earth had happened? Where the heck was the river?
It was way, way down. I was witnessing a disaster!
Fresh run fish being hit by a sudden, massive fall in water would be put off the take, they would be shocked by such an unnatural drop in height.
The river was down more than eighteen inches to low summer water height.
I had never seen such a thing happen before.
I began fishing, but by the time my party arrived at half past nine I had only had one tentative 'pull' to report.
The fish were still there, but they were almightily spooked.

Jimmy MacDonald looked at the river and I knew he was as angry as I was.
It was the work of the dam at Pitlochry.
The conditions every salmon angler could ever have wished for or dreamed of, those that might come just once in a lifetime, were gone.
Although they didn't realise how difficult the day would be the rest of my party understood that things were not good. By lunch we had two fish. We were philosophical about it, but I for one would really have liked to have fished the day that had been set up the night before, because I had never seen fish draw into a place in the middle beats in those sort of numbers.
I would most probably have had at least a double figure spring day myself, but it was gone and there was no sense crying about it.
Exasperated by fishing through hundreds of fish that wouldn't take I put on a black and gold Koster spoon in the afternoon, a heavy one, and fished the Boat pool with fish rising constantly everywhere around me.
In mid-afternoon I got a powerful take that held rock solid.
I fought the fish for some forty minutes and eventually I could see it lying out about fifteen yards from me. It was a good one, but I was making no impression on it. Gradually it came fractionally closer as I waded out closer to it, with my friend David Morris wading out just behind me. It was bigger than any I had caught at that stage and, frustrated by the day that had been forced on us I was desperate to get it and so decided I would gaff it.
This was something I did not like to do and was a measure of my desperation to get something good out of the day.
I told David what I was going to do and extended the Hardy extra-long telescopic gaff I used to carry for emergencies and mainly for self-defence against poachers up on our beat at Dunkeld House.
I got just about close enough with the river up around my chest and stuck the gaff into the fish, which instantly took off with both the gaff and me, pulling me straight under the water.
David grabbed me and for a second or two there was some doubt as to how things were going to go. But we hauled ourselves and the fish out onto the bank where we found it to be bigger than I had thought, weighing exactly thirty pounds. It is still the biggest Atlantic salmon I have caught and will always be so, despite having caught numerous twenty nine pounders, and it was from the same pool where Miss Ballantyne caught her sixty four pounder in 1922!
I had three fish for the day and the party had six, so it ended up a fair one, but we struggled for the rest of the week as the hundreds of fresh run fish remained on edge.
There was a public enquiry by the River Board as to why the dam had dropped the river so much on that day, because it had also badly affected the very best beats on the river quite disastrously. I remember there were a lot of excuses made and phrases like 'necessary maintenance' floated about, but it didn't matter to me because the perfect spring day had gone forever and I would never see its like again.

47. Haow!

David Morris used to work in the looming sheds in the Lancashire textile industry in the 1960's. The din from the looms was horrendous and no one could hear anyone speak, even if they were standing right next to them.
So a piercing yell was developed, it sounded like a sort of 'Haow!', in order to attract the attention of someone standing nearby.
If my memory serves me well the first time he used it was in 1969 on Upper Murthly on the Tay. We were all mad keen anglers, living the adventure that only the great spring Tay salmon could provide, and we were fully engrossed in our quest for the king of fish when from upstream a piercing yell rent the air.
We turned and there was David, almost half a mile above us, but he didn't appear to have a fish on and seemed to be just fishing away. We couldn't understand where the shout had come from and resumed fishing.
Some fifteen minutes later another piercing yell made us jump and look up river again, but there was only David up there fishing and he didn't seem disturbed by whoever was shouting.
Half an hour later the same thing happened, but this time when we looked upstream there was David giving us a half wave, it was he who had been pulling our legs.
We had a laugh about it at lunchtime, but in the afternoon he succeeded in doing it to us twice more and the strange thing was that we fell for it every time.
So there started a game of seeing who you could 'get' by giving the yell.
If they looked round at you, they had been 'got'.
The art was in allowing someone you had just 'got' to resume fishing and become lost in concentration on the adventure again, then waiting for an appropriate length of time to pass to make sure they were not simply trying to anticipate your yell, for if they were a rude gesture would be bound to come your way, and then give them a really loud 'Haow!'.
Of course engaging in this kind of activity was out of the question when there were certain people in the fishing party, nor would it do for certain waters if you wanted to be invited back.
But most ghillies we were acquainted with would even begin advising the people in the boat as to precisely how long they should wait before trying to 'get' someone back.
I wouldn't want you to think that we spent all day yelling at each other, we didn't, but it would be employed at an odd moment as we fished the blank weeks or the weeks of one or two fish, of which there were many.
Jimmy McLean at Dunkeld House appreciated the finer points of the yell as he had a superb sense of humour and the defining moment was reached one Saturday evening in April 1972 when David Morris and I were returning from a fantastic record spring week on Murthly.
We stopped in Dunkeld High Street, walked down the steps by Telford's bridge and up the bank towards Jimmy, who was harling the Cathedral Stream with his angler, a Dr.Cohen, another man with a great sense of humour.
Even though they were above us and with Dr.Cohen facing down the river in our direction, they had not noticed our arrival, so David gave his piercing 'Haow!'.

Cohen jumped and Jimmy spun around from the engine, so we gave them both a friendly, highly satisfied, wave.
When eventually they had fished down to opposite us Jimmy brought the boat close to our bank and we had a brief conversation about Dr. Cohen's current total of seventeen for the week as against our fifty two, but that Ned Vandervell's party fishing Catholes/Pitlochrie Pool had taken over 120 spring salmon, which was unheard of.
It was the greatest spring I would ever be lucky enough to witness on the Tay.
David and I left them in the Sandy Pool below Dunkeld Cathedral to finish off the short stretch down to the bridge and we walked back towards the car talking about the fish and what an incredible week it had been.
We had walked some fifty yards and were engrossed in our conversation when an ear-splitting yell rent the air and we both spun around.
There was Jimmy, looking back at us over the outboard motor giving us a gentle wave.
We had been 'got'!
From that moment I noticed there came a distinct dwindling of the use of 'Haow!' on the river and by the next season it had all but disappeared and we got back to the peace and quiet and more accepted practices of the great adventure that is fishing for the Atlantic salmon.

48. Old Willie

In olden times the village of Birnam, on the other side of the river Tay from Dunkeld, used to be the railhead and travellers would stay at the Birnam Hotel before taking the stagecoach northwards. Upon doing so, and passing through the gap between the mountain of Craigie Barns and the lesser high ground of the Kings Seat behind Dunkeld House, they would promptly be robbed by the 'highwayman' Duncan Ogg, who seemed to have himself a good business.

Old Willie was the Birnam station master through the sixties into the seventies and he was a great character.

Early in the salmon season on Friday and Saturday nights the platform could be full of salmon from all the beats in the middle of the river and they lay packed into salmon basses, waiting for the night train south to London.

There could be lots of them if the river was fishing well, but when it wasn't there could be none!

We once had a young boy who caught his first salmon at Dunkeld House. Starting out as a nice sixteen pounder by the time it got to London it was only seven pounds as some thieving swine swapped it on the journey.

This didn't happen often thankfully.

But Old Willie had a major fault that was as irksome as it was funny.

I remember one time that it happened in particular. I was going down to London on the night train one February, the snow was on the ground and it was freezing cold. Willie ushered me into his station master's office where he had a fine fire going and it was as warm as toast.
Two great friends turned up, local author Douglas Sutherland and his wife Diana, along with several other people and the crack was good.
Willie's phone rang.
"Aha........aha...........right...........right you are then." He put the phone down and announced that the train was at Blair Atholl. We continued talking about the ing to London for. After a while the phone rang again.
"Aha........aha...........right...........right you are then." Willy turned to us and said that the train was now leaving Pitlochry and shortly would be passing Ballinluig. After a confirmatory phone call came in that it had Willie told us we should go out onto the platform.
So we waited and then trooped out into the cold night air, with Willie marshalling us into position to stand roughly where our respective carriages would stop.
Pretty soon the cold would begin to penetrate as we waited expectantly for the train, which eventually we could hear in the distance and then there it was, entering the station and we all stood there like a row of lemons as the train roared straight through without stopping!
Willie had once again forgotten to tell them at Inverness that the night train must stop at Birnam as he had passengers for it!
It was not the only time this happened I can assure you!
Well it was total mayhem!
Everyone grabbed their bags and ran for their cars. I remember people shouting to those who had been dropped off and now had no transport to share their cars. Douglas and Diana jumped into mine.
We now had to race the train the twelve miles to Perth!
Forget the modern day super straight A9 between Dunkeld and Perth, in those days it was the old, winding A9 that passed through Bankfoot and twisted under the viaduct by Luncarty (over the Shochie burn that fish run later in the year!) on its fairly tortuous way down to Perth.
Off we set like the start of a Formula One race. Whether we had consumed alcohol or not didn't seem to matter (many had thinking they wouldn't be driving that night) as down the road we sped, a fast moving convoy the maxim of which was 'devil take the hindmost'!
We tried spotting the train, but couldn't see it as we took the racing line on every slippery bend, pushing our luck as far as it would go on the icy surface. Then we saw the train in the distance ahead of us, then it was gone again.
We descended upon Perth like the biblical Assyrians, pushing hard to make green traffic signals and sitting impatiently at red ones and finally we came roaring into the station car park and screeched to a halt. Out we jumped, grabbed our bags, said to hell with the car park fees and, in a running, shouting, bag carrying rabble made our way as fast as we could into the station past the railway staff, shouting that we were all from Birnam and they should 'get out of the way'!
There was the train standing at the platform! Hooray! Over the foot bridge we struggled, everyone helping everyone else to get down onto the platform and then

we piled into the train through the first available door, the whistle sounded and the train moved off!
Out of breath we helped each other carry our bags along the train to our respective compartments and Douglas, Diana and I had a whisky together and made a toast to forgetful Old Willie, sitting back at Birnam station, nice and warm in his stationmaster's office.
"Stupid old bugger!" said Diana.

49. Unlikely Thieves

After I started Butterstone Loch as a trout fishery back in 1972, netted the pike and created the harbour (which is another story on its own) I began a stocking programme with rainbow trout.
Rick Knight would build rearing cages after my period of tenure ended in 1974 (thanks to Harold Wilson's Labour government's Capital Transfer Tax).
Butterstone is one of a chain of lochs to the East of Dunkeld that stand on the Lunan Burn, a burn that used to run salmon in the old days. The chain starts with CraigLush, then comes the Loch of the Lowes and then Butterstone.
Loch of the Lowes is a famous nature reserve that is often home to breeding pairs of Ospreys.
One day Maurice Drummond, the ranger on Loch of the Lowes came to see me and he was in a bit of a state. He had lost his Slavonian Grebe chicks and had been out scouring the loch for a couple of days looking for them.
He asked if I had seen them, which I hadn't, but I knew where they were, most probably having been eaten by an unlikely thief.
I told him the stories of the size of pike that resided in his loch that the Poles stationed in the area during the war had fished for and that they had caught many huge specimens. I reminded him that the war had been some thirty years ago, during which time pike could grow to a size where they would easily take ducklings, including Slavonian Grebe chicks.
He didn't believe me at first but I told him about the more than one hundred and fifty pike we had taken out of Butterstone up to twenty five pounds using gill nets before we had stocked our trout and he asked if perhaps he could set a gill net in Loch of the Lowes just to see what would happen.
So I lent him a good long gill net and explained how to set it, which he did, returning to it twenty four hours later to find it holding no less than sixteen pike, the largest weighing twenty eight pounds!
He brought this big pike into Dunkeld House in the evening, having shown it to many people around the county during the day, and it lay on the table in the fishing room where everyone came to look at it. Finally he believed me about the pike problem in his loch and I daresay there would be forty or even fifty pound pike in there, so there was no real point in worrying about the survivability of ducklings.
If they were going to survive they would but if the pike were going to have them there was nothing that could be done.
It turned out that the Scottish Wildlife Trust, for whom he worked, were against killing the pike, preferring nature to take its course.

So Slavonian Grebe chicks were liable to become even rarer.
Late that night I carried the pike, wrapped in a plastic sheet, down the dingy back corridor along to the hotel kitchen. The corridor was lit only by one small night light. Suddenly the fish gave a tremendous lurch and shot into the air, making me jump out of my skin! When I examined it its gill plates had begun to move again, even though it had been 'killed' some twelve hours previously!

50. Catalogue of Disaster

Around 1970 the brothers Appleby used to stay with us and fish the lower beats of the Tay.
They were polite, jovial businessmen, slightly rotund and not yet experienced at salmon fishing. Their company, Appleby and Ireland, used to make things like spacesuits for NASA's astronauts and they were highly intelligent men.
One of them fished on his own one day down at Benchil with ghillies Sandy Winter and Alf Campbell.
Alf was a good man, but big Sandy was ever such a bad influence on him.
Hartley Byrom once told me that the two of them had rowed him across the river at Benchil so he could fish the other bank and when he looked in his bag for the unopened bottle of whisky he had brought with him that morning, he found they had emptied the entire bottle behind his back whilst ferrying him across!
Unfortunately for Appleby it seemed that the night before he got there Sandy's wife had thrown him out of the house and he'd gone round to Alf's where they had emptied a number of bottles of Scotch together.
So when Appleby turned up at Benchil at nine o'clock in the morning and produced a brand new, gleaming Ambassadeur reel Sandy, still paralytic, took one look at it and hurled it into the bushes saying they didn't need 'any of that nonsense'.
They then tackled him up and began harling the river.
In the Aitken Head pool Appleby proceeded to hook a good spring fish.
At this Sandy and Alf, who were still fu', rowed in to the river bank, told Appleby to get out, and suddenly took off in the boat into the middle of the river and began shouting to him to get higher and higher up the rocks just below where the great steps that come down from the old car park ended!
Appleby battled away with the fish and watched in utter astonishment as Alf, who was standing waving for him to get higher up (completely the wrong thing to be doing in the first place) fell overboard, making a huge splash!
He became even more astonished after Sandy made strenuous efforts to rescue his friend, which resulted in him falling overboard as well!
The last Appleby saw of the two of them was as both they and the boat floated out of the pool and disappeared away around the corner, heading for Perth.
Appleby did well though and managed to land his fish, which was in the high teens of pounds, and he then waited for almost an hour and a half until here came Sandy and Alf, having been rescued by the ghillies on one of the beats below, rowing their boat back up against the strong stream to take him fishing again.

However even though they had been somewhat sobered up by their experience in the icy waters Appleby declined, told them exactly what he thought of the pair of them and returned to the warm log fire and safety of Dunkeld House to tell us the whole sorry tale.

51. The Desperadoes

There were three of them and they were absolute desperadoes when at the fishing.
They would be out on the river long before first light, stay out all day and only come in long after dark.
They always fished spinning tackle, never the fly, and they would tour down our beat starting at the top and finishing at the Cathedral Stream, almost a mile and half downstream. There they had a guy on a motorbike employed to take them back up to the top of the beat so they didn't miss any fishing time. They would fish down one after the other some 40 yards apart, so the motorcyclist would take the first one to finish back up then come back down for the next one.
They never even stopped for lunch and kept casting while eating sandwiches and they each had a funny looking gadget attached to their waists that swivelled outwards and held a cup of whatever hot liquid or soup they wanted to drink.
Each had a flask with a push-off top clipped to their waist next to the gadget so they could pour their drinks and drink them using one hand.
They would cast out, pour the drink and clip the flask back into position.
Reel in, cast out, drink their drink as their lure came fishing back across the river.
The next thing they would do was to race Jimmy down the beat so that they got to fish the water first, before the boat. As Jimmy approached they'd fish faster and faster down the beat, then take their motorcycle journey back up again.
But that was nothing.
Stopping to go to the toilet seemed to be forbidden.
They were never seen going into the bushes to relieve themselves, presumably thinking that would be time lost fishing!
But there was one even sadder fact about the desperadoes.
In the few years they fished with us at Dunkeld House not one of them caught a fish!

52. Catholes

My first sight of the Catholes weir, as a fishing guest of Ned Vandervell in early February 1970, took my breath away.
This particular crisp Monday morning was blessed with sunshine as we arrived and got out of our vehicles to set up our tackle.
I was just above the weir that ran across the river from bank to bank with the Tay, a rushing torrent of boiling white water, cascading down over it into streamy pools that looked as if they had been specifically made to hold fish.
I had not seen anything I could call a clean run spring fish up in the middle beats since the opening of the season on January 15th, only reasonable numbers of kelts attempting to make their way back to the sea.
In the early part of the year most spring salmon will not run a major obstruction until the water temperature rises to around 42 degrees, urging them to move on. Then they will all go over it together as they do through the fish ladder at Pitlochry dam on the river Tummel towards the end of every April or beginning of May.
If you are in the area at that time go and visit the ladder and you might be lucky to see them passing through one of the two glass sided tanks, nose to tail.
That February we had freezing temperatures on the high ground, although the days were quite nice on the low ground where we lived, and so the river temperature was well below 42 degrees.
I was going cross eyed between trying to look at the river and set my rod up at the same time. Ghillie Geordie Stewart advised me to put on a metal Devon, a black and gold with a red line between the two colours and about two and half inches in length. But whilst I was tying it on I looked down at a small pool just below me when a big spring fish, well into the twenties of pounds, stuck its back out and submerged again only feet from the low wall running along the edge of the pool!
Geordie nodded acknowledgement of its presence and instructed me to go to this pool, the Slaap, and fish it with short casts. I couldn't wait, but as I walked down to it I began to see fish after fish rising out in the middle of the river below the central run of the weir, clean bars of silver lying in the highly oxygenated water waiting for the temperature to rise so they could run up and over the weir and eventually come through the likes of us up at Dunkeld.
There were dozens of fish rising as Geordie took the Vandervells out and moored them below the weir. They would be spinning through hordes of spring salmon and catch them they did.
I got to the Slaap wall and threw the Devon about fifteen yards, over to a shallow ridge that bordered it out in the river. It fished well and three or four clean fish appeared in it, only yards from me. After a while one took me, a bright fish of around ten pounds that ran all over the pool. Whilst it was doing so I could see the Vandervells had a fish on.
I had three fish that day and was ecstatic, handing them to Mr.Vandervell with pride and he accepted them graciously, despite the fact that he and Mrs.Vandervell had seven between them.
This was the beginning of my fishing for a number of parties who had spare rods available on some of the finest beats of the Tay for many years to come, allowing

me to learn how to present my bait to the fish the way they preferred it because of the numbers I would be fishing through.
It is the fish that teach you how to fish for them if you pay attention to what they are doing, what you are doing and the river and overhead conditions each time a fish takes you.

But Catholes could be a thoroughly exasperating place as well.
After the water temperature rose and the bulk of the fish moved on it was the kind of place that might yield nothing for days on end and then suddenly fish would be on the take and the party would get a few and then nothing again for days, or maybe an odd one.
The Corner pool down at the bottom of the beat, actually at the top of the Pitlochrie Pool beat, is a really fishy place. Running off fast shallows the river dives into this deep pool that is surrounded on either side by submerged rocky ledges. Fishing the prawn in it is tricky. You have to throw it upstream towards the neck of the pool, let it sink a way down, hopefully without snagging the jutting ledges, and tighten on it just a little as it comes past you, letting it slowly rise through the middle of the channel. Fish shoot out from their hiding places under the ledges to nail it.
I had some good fish this way in a pool that was not that easy to get fish out of and an old school friend, James Mallett, had a beautiful twenty five pounder there in October 1973 that he did extremely well to land.

53. Expletives on the Wind

In the early seventies I fished Catholes/Pitlochrie Pool with Ned Vandervell's party at a time when the Tay was enjoying a really good run of February spring fish.
At lunchtime Geordie Stewart came across the river in the boat to pick me up and asked if I had seen Mr.Vandervell. Geordie had been looking down the river, but couldn't see him.
I hadn't seen Ned all morning, so we took a trip downstream to look for him.
He wasn't where he was supposed to be and yet we could see a long way down the river bank. Geordie became concerned. Sometimes people collapse with heart attacks when fishing and there is always the awful possibility of them falling into the river or maybe simply losing their footing and the icy winter water temperature could quickly be too much for them.
Where on earth was Ned?
We decided to beach the boat and hunt the river bank. For several minutes we walked up and down the bank, but no Ned. We were standing there talking about what to do next when Geordie said,
"Can you hear something?"
I couldn't, so we listened. There on the wind seemed to be a distant faint whisper. We looked at each other puzzled by this and began to walk into the wind. We stopped and listened and there it was again. As we progressed down the riverside the murmuring became distinct and, coming over a small rise in the ground, there was Ned Vandervell, lying on his back in a hollow muttering to himself.

He saw us and sprang to his feet.
His face was reddened and he starting gesticulating and yelling!
"Big sod! Oh he was a big sod! Never seen anything like him! Out there!" He pointed repeatedly at the river.
"Hooked him up there! Ran down the other bank! Enormous! Bloody enormous!"
We walked up to him and listened as the expletives flowed.
Ned had once owned Catholes/Pitlochrie Pool and was a man well used to landing big thirty and forty pound class spring salmon. An excellent fisher he could handle any size of fish and you would put your money on him to land the most difficult of fish under any circumstances.
But the description of the one he had battled for almost an hour and a half that morning indicated it had probably been in the region of fifty pounds.
Ned had given the fish some real stick, pushing his line to the limits of its breaking strain all the time and the fish had surfaced several times allowing him get a really good look at it. Perhaps it would have been better for Ned had it remained hidden beneath the surface. At times it had been a long way from him right across on the other bank some seventy yards away and moving swiftly downstream. Somehow he had managed to hang on and had got it back to within forty yards. Again the huge fish had come up on the surface, cruising lazily past him on its way upstream this time, seemingly unconcerned with all Ned's efforts to subdue it.
Finally it came up on the surface again and then the hooks came away and Ned's largest ever spring salmon slipped slowly beneath the surface of the Tay.
As Ned said, "it was like watching the Titanic sinking!".
He was so agitated it took us fully ten minutes to calm him down to a level of composure that allowed us to get some sense out of him.
All the way back in the boat he was gesticulating, pointing to where he had hooked the monster, describing what had happened.
As soon as we beached the boat he jumped out and began the same performance with the rest of the fishing party and continued all through lunch.
Geordie summed it up aptly,
"For a fish to be able to do that to a man who has seen hundreds of big spring fish here over the years it must have been one hell of a fish!"

54. Geordie and the Wash House

Geordie Stewart was head boatman/ghillie on the Stanley beat of the Tay that comprises both Catholes and the Pitlochrie Pool beat that fronts Stanley Mill.
I first met him as a guest of Ned Vandervell, whose family used to fish there each February amongst the heavy runs of spring salmon so prolific at the beginning of the 1970's. Rapids with pools at the edge of them where running spring fish might stop off for a second or two, like Kirky or the WashHouse, were a somewhat new phenomenon to me, being used to slower, deeper water up at Dunkeld.
It was the Wash House that proved particularly sporting after lunch the following day. I had wandered outside the stone 'bothy' used as a fishing hut to see if I could spot a fish or two running while the others continued their lunch. The Wash House is a shallow pool lying to the inside of the rapids on the opposite side of the river to the underwater dyke I mentioned before and it ends downstream at a massive concrete pier, below which another mill stream enters the river, coming down the right hand side of the river from the Catholes weir.
Geordie and I decided to have a cast until the party was ready to fish the afternoon. He went below me and shortly hooked a fish in the tail of the pool and began shouting to me to come down and play it. I was not at all keen to have fish hooked for me, even though I would often hand my rod to people over the years so they could play a fish I had hooked, because I never regarded myself as a 'toff'. When I hesitated Geordie became seriously agitated, beckoning and shouting me to come down and take the rod from him. I slowly walked down to him and casually asked what his problem was. He demanded I take the rod, though I protested, but my protestations fell on deaf ears and with some force he thrust it into my hands.
I should have known something was wrong when I saw he had his thumb jammed against the spool of the Ambassadeur reel to stop it from running. The moment he released it the fish took off down the rapids and half the drum emptied in seconds. I sprinted to the concrete pier, leapt up onto it and sprinted down to the end of it, but the line was disappearing unbelievably quickly. Suddenly a big bush rose to the surface in the middle of the river with the fish on the other side of it.
The line had snagged the bush and the next second it parted.
Geordie commiserated and told me I was unlucky, to which I replied with a couple of friendly phrases of expletives. We both knew it had been a big fish and was most probably going to take off down the rapids, making it nigh on impossible to land. I had known it as soon I had seen him deliberately stopping the drum from running.
"Thirty pound class," was all he said under his breath and smiled,
"Oh, Mr.Vandervell! Mr.Miller has just lost us a good fish! We better stick him somewhere safe for the afternoon where he can't do himself any harm!"
I had to endure an afternoon of kidology from the two of them about it.

55. Bob Campbell and Horsey

For some years Bob Campbell ghillied with Geordie Stewart on Catholes/Pitlochrie Pool and we got on well. Geordie had been a boxer in his younger days and I guessed Bob had too as his nose had been broken at some time, so I was fishing amongst fairly tough people and one day I made a mistake with Geordie, even though I hadn't thought of it as being one at the time.

Fishing as a guest of Ned Vandervell on Pitlochrie Pool one February, Geordie instructed me where to fish. I had looked at the light and river conditions we had that morning and really fancied fishing Horsey down at the bottom of the beat, but Geordie wouldn't let me go to it. So I spent a fishless morning on the bank and after lunch Geordie said I was to go in the boat with Bob.

Bob asked me where I would like to fish and I told him I really fancied Horsey and no one had been in it yet that day, so could we go there?

Bob was of the same opinion so off we went to the bottom of the beat.

Horsey lies just above the shallow rapids called the Skellies, before the river dives in white water down into the top of Benchil beat below.

A big, nice looking pool it ends at the barrier of an underwater dyke or ledge, I am never sure which, in the middle of which is a gap through which fish that have been battling their way up the Skellies enter the pool.

Bob went to the bow to drop the anchor and I threw out quite a small wooden Devon.

Bang!

The anchor was not yet down and I was into a fish. Bob was laughing and telling me to give him a chance to get organised. When the fish came near the boat it stayed down deep. We could see it clearly in the sun, but it was determined to stay down, just out of netting range. After a while Bob said if I would release pressure and drop the fish back he would have a go at netting it.

So he plunged the net down into the stream as I eased up on the fish and let it sail back into the net. What with the weight of the fish and the powerful current Bob had a real struggle to get the net up, but he managed to after some seconds, dispatched and unhooked the fish and handed me the little wooden Devon.

I immediately threw it out across the river.

Bang!

A second fish came on!

"For heavens sake, Mr.Miller! Will you no give a ghillie a chance to get organised today?" Bob was laughing at me and shaking his head. Whenever a ghillie called me Mr.Miller, especially in a mock serious voice as if they were addressing some toff, they were always taking the mickey.

This fish again stayed deep when it came to the boat and we went through the same performance with Bob having a real struggle not to lose both fish and net this time. Then he deliberated whether he ought to give me the Devon back straightaway or get himself organised first, but condescended to once more hand me the Devon, which I threw straight out across the river.

Bang!

I hooked another one!

Now we were both laughing at the almost ridiculous situation of my having hooked three fish in three casts at a time when fish had been scarce. Once again I could not lift the fish when it came to the boat, each of them had seemed to turn their pectoral fins to take them deep into the current and this time Bob nearly went over the side when he tried to net it, so I grabbed him and we got the fish inboard.
Three fish of ten to twelve pounds weight were a sheer delight for us.
Then Bob grabbed a hold of my rod and threw out a cast with the wooden Devon.
Bang!
Another fish came on, but unfortunately it dropped off after a couple of minutes and then the run was through and we caught nothing more.
Meeting up with Geordie and Mr.Vandervell's party, who were fishless, Geordie asked me where we got the three fish and that was when I made my mistake.
"In Horsey, where you wouldn't let me go in the morning," I said.
Things were never quite the same between Geordie and me after that, even though I had not meant it in any other way than pulling his leg.

56. A Cargill Day

Colin Leslie was the ghillie on Cargill when I used to fish it and I had some phenomenal summer fishing with him over the years.
I fished there one day with Colonel Peter Castle Smith, Paul Zissler, Johnny Cooke-Hurle and Alan Allison.
I got down to the beat early in the morning and immediately caught a ten pound sea liced fish on fly before our fishing day had officially begun. When Colin arrived he said he wanted to show me a spot under the railway bridge, but that we should keep well away from the river as we walked up to it. In those days I used a seventeen and half foot double handed carbon fibre salmon fly rod, but Colin had me standing back from the river in my chest waders, flipping out no more than two metres of line from the end of it.
My fly was barely reaching the river, but Colin told me to stand stock still because if there was a grilse resting at the edge of the stream it would come for it.
Paul and Alan came and sat on the bank just below us and began making caustic comments such as 'do you realise the river was actually over there?'.
Colin said not to pay attention and give it half a dozen more flips with the short line and then we would go.
I saw the grilse come like a flash of lighting out of the stream and nail the fly.
As the rod bent Paul and Alan went quiet and Colin said 'I told you so' as we landed a five and a half pound sea liced grilse.
Salmon will rest in very shallow water as long as they are not disturbed and it is worth making a cautious approach to any pool and start with a short line before fishing your way out into it, rather than go crashing in and wading out through the very place where fish could be lying.
Peter Castle Smith has taught me more about flies and fly fishing than anyone, especially Spey casting, which he finds as lazy a way of casting as I do.
Neither of us have ever been into the 'mystique' of the art of salmon fly fishing that so many people would have you believe exists.

I have taught lots of people to cast perfectly far enough to catch a salmon in under ten minutes, so how mystical can it be?
Peter used to fish the same length of rod as I did and being a big, strong man, waded all over the river to cast his fly out over every available lie including those most others couldn't reach.
The funny thing that happened that day was when he did hook a fish and began to fight it he found to his dismay that there was no resistance and that the fish he had on was extremely small.
I was in the boat with Colin and we watched as the Colonel backed himself delicately out of the river.
Here was this great big man, who used to catch huge sea trout on the Spey back in the fifties, finding himself trying to land a fish of about two pounds with this great big rod that was way too powerful for such a small fish.
Though embarrassed he graciously finished backing out of the river and then let the little fish play itself out, rather than haul it ignominiously straight out of the river. Having given it a chance to show off its fighting powers he finally beached the little two pound grilse and promptly released it back into the Tay to live and fight another day, to a round of applause from up and down the river.
"We see your getting into the really big ones now, Peter!" we shouted from the boat.
Finally that day Johnny Cooke-Hurle, at a strapping six feet six inches tall decided he would see if six feet six computes into fourteen feet of water by wandering off the end of a ledge that Colin had told him not to go out past, but he demonstrated a fine natural swimming stroke as he got himself back to dry land, having found that six feet six goes into fourteen feet more than twice!

57. Fame at Last!

As a member of Perth Angling Club in the 1970's I used to get summer permits to fish the Redgorton beat of the Tay. The Club members who fished there were a varied and great bunch, most of whom were expert salmon fishers.

The Black Craigs is the top pool of the beat and it begins and ends with a croy, stones built up and out into the river, around the point of which the current is strong. Fish running the right hand bank come up around the point of the lower croy and swing in towards the bank a little, giving you a good chance at them. However the pool of the Craigs is only some eighty yards or so long and we needed a fair system of fishing so that everyone got their chance.

So we used the classic for salmon fishing.

You waded in at the top of the Craigs and every couple of casts took a couple of steps down the river. After covering an acceptable distance, maybe a dozen or fifteen yards down the pool the next person waded in and so on, following you down the pool, and you each came out after reaching the bottom croy.

In order to guarantee yourself a really good chance of a fish you had to watch for them coming a long way down the river then wade in and time your movement down the pool so that you got to the hot spot, where your bait was just above the bottom croy, at the same time as the run of fish were coming around the point of it and hopefully a fresh fish would grab it.

Once I was standing at the top of the Craigs looking down the river, waiting for fish to come, and I kept very graciously letting people wade into the pool in front of me. They knew fine why I was waiting and begrudgingly went ahead at my insistence. One couple had stood talking with me for several minutes before taking their turn and when I turned my attention back to the river again I immediately saw the flick of a tail of a running fish, but he was only a hundred yards below the bottom croy. I wouldn't get to the hot spot in time!

The minutes passed as I waited for the couple to get an acceptable distance down the pool for me to be able to wade in, during which I saw another fish head-and-tail, but this one was even closer to the bottom croy. Eventually I did get in and decided I would throw long casts and let line slip away so that the shrimp I was fishing would be below most of the five or six people below me and that I would take the risk of tangling up with them in my efforts to hook a fish.

I waded out until the river was a couple of inches from the top of my chest waders so that I was out past the line of anglers below me and began to fish.

The first fish came around the bottom croy and made a running jump into the pool. I cast out again and let the shrimp sail away down the river. Then I went to take a step and put my foot on something that rolled away from under me into deeper water, lost my footing and disappeared under the water!

Surfacing with my rod in one hand and striking out for the bank with my free arm the current gripped me and turned me around and around as I thrashed my way down the pool past each of the anglers below me.

They burst into a round of applause, tucking their rods under their arms and clapping loudly as I churned the water to a foam and finally reached the bottom croy, where my feet touched the river bed again. My chest waders were full of water and I was soaked to the skin as I listened to the chuckles going on up above me. It was a hot summer day so I stripped off most of my clothing, began to wring the water out of it and began the process of drying everything on the bushes in the sun.

More than a decade later I was shopping in Perth and noticed a man who kept looking at me and smiling.

"You don't remember me, do you?" he said, chuckling.

"No, I'm sorry, where did we meet?"

"Oh," he said, "I was present at a very special occasion some years back."

I ran through the few special occasions I could think of in my mind, but he just kept shaking his head and laughing.

"I was there the day you went for a swim down the Black Craigs in your waders!" he said gleefully.

Ah, fame at last....

58. Low Water Flies

Johnny Oblanski 'The Pole' lived up at Pitlochry and caught many a fish in his time. Jimmy McLean knew him well and had talked to me of him on occasion.
Whenever the boat at Dunkeld House was not taken by a guest I would go out and ghillie for myself, hooking a fish proving an interesting experience of controlling the boat, getting the other two rods in and fighting and landing the fish.
Once, upon beaching the boat at the front of the hotel, I was in a hurry and inexplicably threw a fixed gaff onto the bank and the hook stuck into the back of my hand.
Can I give you a piece of advice?
If you ever throw a fixed gaff anywhere, not that you would be that stupid, throw it hook first!
Towards the end of the period my wound took to heal Jimmy suggested we go up and fish Pitlochry Dam off the Blue Stones on the left hand bank for an evening and that Johnny Oblanski could get us a permit. So we went up and I met Johnny and we chatted about the fishing. Jimmy had put a low water salmon fly on my rod, a silver March Brown (tied with a silver rib), and the two of them left me at the top notice board that warned anglers not to fish any closer to the dam, and went back to the bottom pool above the pedestrian bridge.
This was the day I came to really appreciate low water dressed flies.
The low water fly is dressed on a long shank hook and the dressing is quite small to the front of the shank behind the eye the cast is tied to and is designed to be fished on a floating line, perhaps with the leader greased to float to within inches of the fly, so that the fly fishes barely an inch or two under the surface.
These flies can take fish in low water conditions when no other fly can.
I have found they also take fish in not so low water conditions as well.
The streams run fast up at the dam, beautiful, bubbling, oxygenated water in which fish lie waiting to run the 'ladder' of tanks that will take them up and through the dam, out into loch Faskally and on up into the higher tributaries such as the river Garry. You can watch them from the viewing room where two tanks have glass sides, but get there in late April or early May to see all the spring fish that have piled in below the dam up to that time of the year moving through together as the water temperature rises. If you are lucky you will see all sizes of fish constantly moving through nose to tail.
I took up position above a boiling run of white water and began to fish.
The casting was difficult at first as my injured hand let me know it wasn't too happy about being loosened up.
Gradually it eased off though and I began to throw a half decent line.
Down in the middle of the run, only maybe twenty five yards below me, I could see a small, glassy slot and fancied that if I was a fish that is where I would be sitting.
So I kept covering it, mending the fly line against the strong stream so my fly would sit in the slot for a few seconds each time it fished through it.
I had done this a couple of dozen times or more when there came the most horrendously powerful take and a substantial bar of silver leapt from the river like a missile heading for outer space with the low water fly in its mouth.
I yelled and Jimmy and Johnny looked up.

The fish, somewhere in the high twenties of pounds, took off out into the fast flowing main stream, turned and exploded down the middle of the river. There was no way I could run after it as the stones below me were treacherous, all I could do was begin to pick my way carefully along them. The fish had now disappeared into the bottom pool and was leaping out of the water in front of Jimmy and Johnny, crashing about like a mad thing only yards from them.
Then it did exactly what it was trying to do and threw the hook.
I wound in the hundred yards or so of line it had taken and got down to them. Johnny looked at me and said,
"By God, you had a hold of him there, Jess. What a great fish, you would never have landed him though, he went berserk right here in front of us. But you did well to hook him, what are you fishing?"
I showed him the low water March Brown and he and Jimmy looked at each other, Jimmy giving me a wink.
"Johnny, that fish took this in the white water up at the top and I'm amazed. I find it incredible it could even see it. I think I'll fish low water flies a bit more from now on!" He agreed with me.
Injuring yourself when fishing might be ignominious, but if I hadn't hooked my hand with that gaff I would never have gone up to the dam that evening and come into contact with a fish that taught me the respect low water flies deserve.

59. The Prawn King

George MacInnes was with Tayside police in Perth. He earned the title the Prawn King during the early 1970's on the Tay. The reason was that George turned prawn fishing into an art and became an expert at it.

When I first watched him from the opposite bank of Redgorton's Black Craigs he took three fish one after another and I had none. He then took off down the bank and away round the corner and came back with another three and took another four in the afternoon.

I once saw him take twelve fish one after another on Benchil.

The thing that George understood was that first you must find the colour the fish are on, then you must fish exactly the right weight of running barrel lead to take the prawn to the level the fish are at and then you must be able to feel the sometimes delicate take and set the hook. A lot of the time the fish hook themselves, but sometimes there comes a very gentle mouthing of the prawn and that is the time you must strike. Many prawn fishers don't even feel it happening and fish on in ignorance. Fortunately I have fished a lot for British Columbia's steelhead and have learned to recognise that gentle nudge when drift fishing.

So I watched George as we fished the summer permits for two and half months and that first season became bemused and exasperated as he caught four to one against me. He turned out to be a great guy with a wicked sense of humour and I learned much from him over the years and we shared many a dram together. It was George who introduced me to 'Rusty Nail', Drambuie and Whisky mixed neat. It tasted quite nice, but kicked like a mule. However it fairly fired up my insides on the occasion when the wind chill factor on the river took the temperature below zero.

I used to watch George as he in turn watched the river and learned that he was looking into the distance to see a head-and-tailer or just the flick of a tail of a running fish and then he would either go straight down to them or meet them somewhere where he felt they might stop.

I learned from him the really good advice I have used and given to many people since.

When fish are coming off the sea in the lower beats of a river they are massed together, but they begin to string out with the born leaders running on ahead and the less desperate or agile ones dawdling along behind.

Once the leaders find they are getting ahead of the group and they enter a suitable pool or place to stop and wait for the others they will take the first thing they see.

Back in those days a prawn or a shrimp (now banned from the Tay) was deadly for taking these momentarily stopped runners.

You can tell these fish because they rise differently. Runners will head-and-tail either in a straight line, or sideways as they cut across streams, give a flick of their tails or make a running jump, travelling well forward in the air. Stopped runners make a good jump out of the water with more vertical and little forward motion and they might rise quite a few times in the same place before moving on.

They will wait there as their numbers build up with the stragglers catching up again and you are as likely to take four or six fish out of them one after another as you are to take one. Never waste your time once you have landed a fish.
Get another prawn or shrimp on and get back in there and present it to them again. The same with lure or fly.
After a short period of time what you will see are fish rising at the head of the place you are in, making splashy rises not really like runners. I think that this is to signal the others that they are moving on. You might get one or two more to take you before they leave and then they will be gone, but when they stop like this after coming straight off the sea you can potentially take a few of them.
This is the fish behaviour the Prawn King would search for and if he saw it he would be off in a flash to get to them.
George and I fished Benchil together for a week one summer and on one day we had twenty nine fish including a twenty nine pounder that fell to a red devon fished by Willy Wilson, head boatman at Loch Leven, who became hysterical as I tried and failed to net it a dozen times as it careered around a quiet backwater before I finally succeeded.
In those days we used to have to walk up and down some fifty or sixty giant steps, with a couple of paces between them, to get to and from the river.
A legendary ghillie, Sandy Winter from Stanley, was with us that day.
Sandy, bless him, could really drink and as the day wore on became somewhat inebriated (I am being polite).
A big man he was a handful when under the influence.
George and I began carrying all the fish up the long haul to the cars and it was hard work.
The longer you carry a fish the heavier it gets as you probably know.
Well we struggled to get the last of the fish up at the end of a hard three quarters of an hour.
I was extremely fit in those days, but it was still quite an effort.
Then we had Sandy to contend with.
He was in maudlin' mood, recounting tales of monster fish caught on Benchil and places where you could catch one. We set off and got him to the bottom of the steps, having stopped three times on the way to be regaled by slurred stories about all kinds of fantastic salmon adventures. Climbing up all those steps with a big, heavy, swaying man who kept insisting on stopping and turning back to the river to point out good places where we could catch fish, whilst swaying around alarmingly, was no fun at all.
Every two or three steps we had to stop. At one stage George grabbed Sandy as he almost toppled backwards down the steps and George began to go over himself until I grabbed the pair of them and we got back on track.
It took us almost an hour to get Sandy to the top of the steps where George folded him into his car to take him home.
We were both exhausted.

60. The Purple Prawn

Though shrimp and prawn fishing is now banned on the river Tay it was one of the main methods of fishing employed up to and throughout the 1970's, especially on the lower, more prolific beats.
Prawn fishing had been around for a very long time indeed with manufacturer's catalogues advertising bottled prawns and sprats back before 1900.
'Rhombo' Brown, once managing director of En-Tout-Cas, used to like to harl one on the centre fly rod at Dunkeld House during a lean week.
He called it his 'roving prawn' and enjoyed good success with it on occasion, but nothing like the success achieved by the prawn fishers down in the lower beats, who had real numbers of fish to work amongst. These were highly experienced anglers, many from Perth Angling Club, who used to get summer permits on Redgorton and Waulkmill and permits from Tay Salmon Fisheries to fish Catholes, Pitlochrie Pool and Benchil during the summers.
So these famous beats were being fished by people who had fished the river all their lives, through the supposedly lean summers, a time when it was thought that renting them to fishing parties might be difficult. However they have been let to fishing parties through the summers ever since the riparian owners and their agents realised in the 1980's that summer fishing might not be quite as lean as they had originally thought.
One August in the mid-1970's I was fishing Benchil and was down in the Little Shot at the bottom of the beat after which the river disappears around a right hand bend into the Black Craigs at the top of Redgorton.

The river was in good ply for summer fishing and there were quite a lot of fish lying in the strong streams, however they were proving difficult to take. We used to dye prawns in varying shades of red or purple, finding that fish would take a particular shade of red better one year and then be on purple the next, but it seemed that whatever I had to offer they were not interested.

What was proving a real challenge was a fish in the forty pound class that would rise maybe once an hour in the channel on the far side of the pool with a big, lazy 'slunge' on the surface. I was able to wade out to a shallow bank in the middle of the river and fish the channel where he was lying. It was probably no more than thirty yards across, so I had my quarry within easy reach, but like the rest he just wasn't interested. I was putting the prawn right on his nose to the best of my ability and time and again it must have either been passing inches in front of him or he was getting out of the way of it.

Hooking the bottom occasionally I would wade back across the river to tie up a new prawn. I fished a running barrel lead above a swivel some two and a half feet from the prawn, which was mounted on a pin and with a treble hook at its head, the first thing to come to the fish, and bound with a fine darkish, almost invisible wire that had come from the inside of an old television set, which lasted me some 20 years!

A couple of dozen times I tied up new prawns and would only go back into the river if they passed my 'that looks good enough to eat' test, despite their being purple.

I fished on and the great fish kept slunging on the surface every once in a while, just to let me know he was still there and that I was not half as clever as I thought I was at prawn fishing. When he finally decided the time had come to engage hostilities and take the prawn it was with a power that ripped line straight off my Ambassadeur.

I had him!

Or, wait a minute, did he have me?

He wasn't moving, just staying where he was with all the pressure I was giving him on eighteen pound breaking strain line having no effect. We stayed like that for fifteen minutes or more, during which I decided that if his lordship were to suddenly decide to clear off out of the pool and down around the bend into the Black Craigs I would be completely snookered.

Little did I know it, but the fish was thinking exactly the same thing.

I eased the clutch on my reel off a little, put the rod over my shoulder, turned towards the river bank and, with my wading staff in my downstream hand, began to make for dry land. I got about ten paces when the great fish decided this was the perfect moment to vacate the locality.

The reel literally screamed in my ear and I just about held onto the rod as the fish exploded from the pool, sped down the fast water, around the bend and was gone into the far distance in about three seconds.

Now I was stuck where I was as I watched the line peeling from the reel because if I went nearer the bank the line would snag the rocks below me down on the bend, which in a few more seconds it did anyway and, being under such pressure, parted with a loud 'twang'!

With three quarters of my line gone I waded to the bank and sat down contemplating the dismal fact that I had lost yet another forty pound class fish and wondered if I would ever land one (I never did).
I was sitting there thinking about the meaning of life when a man wearing chest waders came puffing up the riverside towards me.
He was red in the face and highly agitated, shouting and gesticulating.
"Hi! Who's fishing a purple prawn! God, what a fish! Never saw anything like it! Beggar jumped right over me! Nearly knocked me over! I almost had a heart attack! It had this purple prawn hanging from its mouth! God, it was huge! Huge!"
I have to be honest in that his description of the size of the fish didn't cheer me at all, still I owned up to the fact that the particular purple prawn he was talking about had once been my property and it had been I who had been attached to the other end of the line.
He was a nice bloke and it must have been a great shock to him to be out in the river fishing away peacefully and suddenly a forty pound salmon takes a huge downstream leap virtually right over him.
From his account it travelled several yards through the air such was the speed it was going at, undoubtedly making for Greenland, and he clearly saw the purple prawn hanging from the side of its mouth.
If there is a moral to be learned from this story it may be this:
Never get cocky and think you are necessarily any smarter than a fish.
You may well be for most of the time, but one day you may find that when it comes right down to the wire you're not quite as smart as you thought you were!
Take my word for it!

61. The Length of Loch Tay

The river Dochart flows in at the top, western, end of Loch Tay at Killin, whose claim to fame came when Kenneth More parked his bicycle against the low wall by the Falls of Dochart in the 1959 movie 'The Thirty Nine Steps'.
The loch winds its way some 14 miles (24km.) past the mountain of Ben Lawers down to Kenmore at the Eastern end, the start of the river Tay.

Back in the good old days of the 1950's there was an elderly ghillie who had trolled for salmon on the loch for decades at the western end. He used to row, using the long greenheart rods and wide diameter brass and ebonite trolling reels of the day.
At the beginning of one season he had no clients to take out, so on the opening day, the 15th January, he decided to go out on his own.
No sooner had he started trolling a couple of Sprats, one on either side of the boat, than he hooked a fish.
He got the other rod in to find the fish was heading out towards the middle of the loch at some speed and he was losing more line than he should be.
As he had been rowing and had no outboard engine he went up to the bow and put the fish under a lot of pressure, the result was that his boat began to move very slowly towards the fish.
Half an hour later he was well out into the loch, being towed slowly along by the fish. He was holding the handle of the trolling reel tight so the fish couldn't take any line, but it was taking him and his boat wherever it was going, which seemed to be right down the middle of the loch. This went on and on with the fish showing no sign of tiring or slowing and by lunchtime he had been towed almost halfway down the loch!
He decided as there was nothing he could do about it that, even though it was cold with snow on the air, he should enjoy the scenery, drink from his flask of coffee and enjoy his lunch.
He had started early when none of the other boats at the western end had been out and by the time they were he had been well down the loch. He never saw another boat until after lunch when he waved to some people who were trolling, but they were some distance away from him.
By mid-afternoon he was 10 miles from Killin and still the fish was continuing down the middle of the loch, heading for the start of the river Tay at Kenmore.
The temperature was now below freezing.
That early in the year the light went by 4.00p.m. and he sat alone in the dark a couple of miles from Kenmore and kept his eye on the distant lights from the houses there. As eventually he slowly came to the eastern shore and the start of the Tay he kept pulling on one oar to ease the boat slowly into the bank away from the river mouth. He got out and gave the fish some real stick. He had never managed to gain any line all day long, but now he could make something of it. Still as each time he gained line it took it away again and it was more than half an hour before he could get its head up onto the shingle beach and grab it and it took all of his strength to haul it out of the water.
In the faint light from the houses he could see it was truly colossal, a huge, long, deep spring fish that would be in the record books for many a year to come.

Being frozen and exhausted he walked up to the Kenmore Hotel where they greeted him and he told his story. So with the proprietor and a couple of others he walked back down to the fish.
It was not there! It had gone!
They shone their torches around, but there was no fish to be seen!
However there were fish scales on the shore, proving this was no fishing tale.
When they asked whether he had knocked the fish on the head to dispatch it though he looked a bit sheepish. No, he had been so tired and frozen and with the fish just laying there, completely out of the water, he had gone to get help and especially to get warm and had forgotten to kill it.
They came to the conclusion that the fish had probably become agitated after he left and its flapping had simply given it enough movement to start it sliding back towards and into the water and it must have swum off.
The old ghillie was devastated.
They kept asking him how big it had been, they could even see from the size of its scales that it had been some size. How long had he fought it? What bait did it take? How had he managed to keep going all day? How deep a fish had it been? All kinds of questions.
They asked about the length of the fish, wanting to know an approximation so they could try to work out what weight it had been. But by this time the old ghillie, cold and exhausted and utterly devastated at the disastrous outcome of his day spent fighting the fish, gave just one curt answer when again they pressed him about how long the fish had been and said,
'The Length of Loch Tay!'.

62. Wedding Distraction

Sometime back in the 1970's we had summer low water conditions yet again.
We would suffer fourteen out of seventeen such summers during our tenure of Dunkeld House. Years later, when I was on the Tay Salmon Advisory Committee, our study of the rainwater gauges that had been in action since 1910 throughout the Tay catchment area (of which we had been unaware) proved that from 1972 there had been a dramatic fall off in rainfall, unprecedented during all that time.
This particular year it was no different. No streams to fish as our beat, which was mainly a higher water, spring and autumn beat, languished lake-like for the most part. Jimmy McIntyre was ghillie on the Upper Dunkeld beat above us and his daughter was getting married one Saturday and the wedding reception was being held in the hotel.
Being a clever little Miller I decided that if Mr.McIntyre was at the wedding he would not be on Upper Dunkeld that afternoon and the Clachantaggart Stone, where I knew the stream would be strong, beckoned.
I would have to be adroit though and decided not to even let my great friend Jimmy McLean see me and crept out of the fishing room after he had gone out on the river, heading for the hills. Well actually up onto the high ground of the King's Seat to make my way over it, through the tree plantation and eventually down onto General Wade's road well past the Rock Pool.

I had carefully spied Jimmy finishing harling the Rock and making his way down into the Ferry, but remained hidden at all times.
I reached the Clachantaggart stone below the 'new' A9 bridge above Dunkeld and there was the strong stream with fish rising in it! I hadn't seen a fish in weeks as our beat lacked the faster, more oxygenated water they loved in summer. I crept out on the line of rocks that links the big rock with the river bank and threw out a red Devon. Third cast a fish took it and in a while I had a fourteen pounder, a little coloured from being in the river a while, but a fish nevertheless and crept back down to the Rock Pool with it to lay it on the bank and fish there for a while.
A couple of guests came walking up the river bank and complimented me on the fish and eventually I made my way back to the fishing room to find the wedding reception going full tilt. I washed the fish off and left it in the sink and a while later Jimmy came in from the fishing.
He looked carefully at the fish, looked at me and said,
"That's a fine fish you've got there, Mr.Miller. What a pity it is you didn't catch it on your own beat!"
How the hell did he know?

63. Big Fish Sprint

Fishing the Summer Permits on Redgorton I remember one particular early summer morning when I got down there around 4.00a.m.
There was thick mist hanging over the river. It would burn off in mid-morning and the forecast was for heat later on, but visibility was only twenty yards or so initially.
There were a few of 'the boys' there and my friend Davy Wilson, who I had first met in P.D.Malloch's famous tackle shop when we had both been boys.
We began launching big Devons out into the mist. We could hear fish splashing regularly, but could see nothing. As we fished on the mist began to lift ever so slowly, still we threw the Devons out into oblivion in hope.
Eventually we could see the other bank of the river and now there were anglers every thirty yards or so above and below Davy and I. Suddenly I felt the most ferocious of takes and the rod bucked in my hands as line began to peel from my Ambassadeur faster and faster.
Davy shouted whether everything was under control.
My answer was a few short expletives as I backed rapidly out of the water.
Reaching the bank I found I was now down to about one quarter of the reel's line capacity and it was still going out fast as the fish hurtled down the middle of the river. I ran and Davy ran after me.
At that time I was training at the Meadowbank Stadium in Edinburgh and often acted as a 'hare' for David Jenkins (then the fastest UK 200 and 400 metre runner).
I was fit and fast, although hampered by chest waders, and as I took off I yelled,
"Look out, lads!"
The anglers below me all dropped their rod points as I 'sprinted' as best I could down along the bank in a desperate effort to stop losing line and catch up with the fish. One hundred, two hundred, three hundred yards Davy and I went and only

when we arrived at a point more than four hundred yards from where I had hooked the fish did it stop.
It fought in a kind of funny way, strong, sudden rushes followed by hardly any resistance and after a while I got it into a big backwater. It surfaced and we could see I had hooked it by the dorsal fin in the middle of its back. After great difficulty Davy managed to slip a gaff hook under its jaw and drag it to the bank, a magnificent twenty seven pound summer Tay fish.
"You know that strictly speaking foul hooked fish have to be put back, don't you?" said Davy, with a grin.
"Of course I know that! So which of us is going to carry it back to my car then?"
The day proved really hard with some forty anglers only landing maybe six fish as the big body of fish that kept on rising and rising took short in the blistering blue day. They would just give you a pull or a rug or a tug and leave your bait alone. I had to leave in the late afternoon, but apparently once the sun dipped and its strong light went off the water the fish came on the take and everyone had a field day.
Returning to the hotel I put the fish in the sink and smoothed down the dorsal fin so that not a mark was showing. In from the fishing came Jimmy McLean and he complimented me on my fish, had a good look at it and said,
"Well, it's another very nice fish you've got there, Mr.Miller, it's just a pity it wasn't hooked in the mouth!"
How the hell did he know?

64. Old Roy

I used to fish the great trout fishery of Loch Leven at a time when it still had the original fantastic Loch Leven trout in it that had been exported to stock all kinds of fisheries all over the world since before the turn of the twentieth century. These were big, silvery, superb brown trout (not a contradiction in colours as they were a unique strain of brown trout).

Now they are gone, due to changed agricultural practices and drainage in the main, and today Loch Leven is a stocked rainbow trout fishery. I used to fish evenings with Alan Allison and old Roy, a kindly soul who unfortunately did not keep too well. Roy would sit in the bow casting no more than three or four yards of line, whilst I would demonstrate the art of defying gravity with a fly line and cast all over God's creation in search of a taking trout.

How many times Roy wiped my eye by catching more than I did I cannot tell you exactly, but it was a lot.

He would just keep flicking that short line out, hooking trout after trout right next to the boat. The trout that rises thirty yards from you perhaps ought to be ignored, after all old Roy never bothered fishing for them. You shouldn't think that fish are only present at great distance from you, there are others really close to you as I have shown many people over the years, having learned first from fishers like Roy!

Yes, you see them splashing under the other bank of a river or in the distance on a loch, but what about those that are lying quietly right next to you?

It is always worthwhile making some short casts first, or permanently!

65. Old John

On the summer permits down at Redgorton people used to go crashing into the river, wading out until the water was up to their middle and then begin fishing. Old John, the schoolteacher, had a different approach.

During the hot summers he would wear a pair of Wellington boots or thigh waders and fish with a single handed trout rod in the edge of the river, behind those who were busy lashing it to foam thirty yards or so further out.

And he would catch fish.

The best day I personally saw him have was four sea trout and two grilse, all taken from behind the other anglers. He told me never to rush into the river, but to fish my way out with a short line at first and that if fish were left quiet they would come right into the shallow water, even in the bright sun of summer, There was another example of this in 'A Cargill Day' on page 79.

66. Fly Over All

In fact it was Colin Leslie's brother Norman who told me another way the fly can score and this I used time and time again, to the great frustration of others.
There was so much shrimping and prawning going on (now banned) that it sometimes became a nuisance to fly fishers.
The thing to do was to watch a pool that had fish rising in it being hammered with the shrimp or prawn by two or three anglers.
Maybe they would catch fish, but it didn't matter whether they did or not.
Eventually they would leave and move off to another pool.
Then you waited for quarter of an hour or so to let the fish calm down.
A small fly on a floating line would be what you should fish.
You went in and gently fished it quietly down and invariably you would take a fish, or maybe two, always giving those who had perhaps left empty handed a friendly wave, just to cheer them up!
Fish in the pool that had been greatly disturbed by all the ironmongery of the shrimps and prawns being fished through them time after time had been settling down while you were letting things quieten, but they were still on the lookout for those big shrimps and prawns appearing again.
When nothing came for a quarter of an hour or so and then a tiny fly appeared, travelling along just under the surface, they often couldn't resist it.
Even today with the prawn and shrimp banned take your time to let a pool quieten after a boat has fished it through, or after anglers who are spinning have finished and then fish it down with a small fly and you will be odds on to take a fish.
You just need to have faith in it.
Anyone can go down to any river, cast anything into it and catch a big salmon. It has been done so many times and novices are usually the ones who do it best.
But the man who consistently presents his fly the way fish want it will take far more fish in a season than the lucky novice because the odds are on his side.
The classic way to present your fly is to cast out then mend your line upstream, perhaps a couple of times, and let the fly come swimming slowly across the river.
However if things are slow with fish not taking, especially if they have been offered everything imaginable, try casting out and this time mending your line downstream. This speeds the fly up and if you strip line in slowly you can assist the speed. Practice varying speeds to find what works best.

67. A Different Way

Once, up on the Spey, Richard Jeffries asked me to go and fish his rod for a morning on one of the Tulchan beats. The party were surly and dour faced and seemed most displeased to see me, but I have broad shoulders and can be as thick skinned as anyone when I want to be. The ghillie walked with me down the river, into a boat and rowed me across, indicating the pool I should fish.

He went back across the river and disappeared.

There were a lot of dark looking fish that had been in for some time rising constantly and I fished down through them without so much as a touch. So I went back up to the top, put on a Teal Blue and Silver fly tied on a double hook and began casting my line square across the river.

Then I mended downstream and stripped the line in slowly, making the Teal Blue come shooting off the far bank.

The first fish that came on was nineteen pounds and so was the second one.

All it was about was the fact that they were seeing something perform differently. They had most probably seen every beautifully tied fly in Scotland fished perfectly over them for days.

What they hadn't seen was something a bit bright and garish that suddenly appeared in front of them only to go shooting away from them across the river, which they found was just too much so they had to take it.

The ghillie came back while I was landing the second fish and looked through binoculars at me landing it. I knew he was looking to see whether I had foul hooked it so I made it absolutely clear I was taking the hook out of the fish's mouth. Back at the fishing hut the party still had nothing and the stony faces became even stonier when they saw my brace of fish.

68. The Backing Up

On the wonderful river Helmsdale they do the 'backing up' and it works fantastically well.

This is where you're fishing very slow water, canal like in some places, but instead of starting at the top of the pool you start at the bottom.

You cast, but don't mend the line, just strip it in slowly and at the same time walk slowly backwards.

Although the fly line is coming across the fish first as you slowly 'back up' the river, believe me when I tell you they will really take it.

Try it somewhere on a river where there is seemingly no current and you know fish are in there.

You may get a surprise!

69. Scotland's Secret Weapon

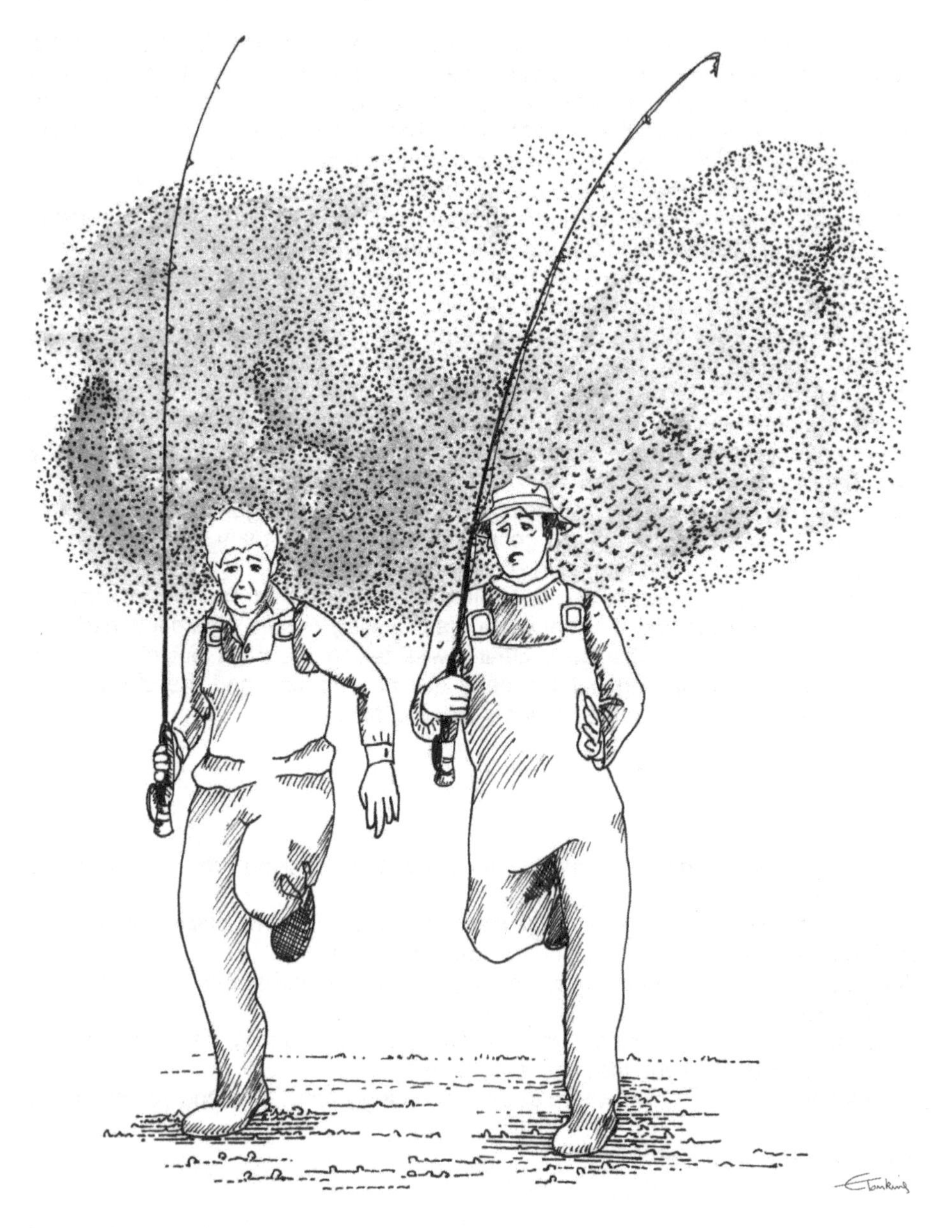

It would be wrong of me to say that Scottish midges were invented purely to harass the English because they are not that selective.
They harass everyone.

Nationality, creed, colour, political persuasion, sex, stature, wealth or looks, none of them matter.
If the highland midge wants you.......it will get you.
A great many years ago I fished the Upper Oykel with Alan Allison of Loch Leven note with barely enough water in the river for fish to run. We had worked away steadily during the morning without a touch from a fish and at lunchtime considered whether we should walk down to a pool on a bend some half a mile or more below us. The wind had been blowing a strong breeze and we thought it might well be worth the foot slog, although in the back of my mind was the possible problem of midges and I said so to Alan.
We both knew full well that highland midges were deliberately created aerodynamically imperfect and cannot fly in wind speeds in excess of three miles an hour, having to dive for cover into the long grasses, heathers and bogs in order to be able to land without crashing.
Once safely hidden from the wind they sit and spend their time sharpening their teeth, in fact I think they probably take turns sharpening each other's to make absolutely sure they are more razor sharp than razors. They then lie back and dream of sinking their fangs into succulent human flesh, rather as we might think of doing to a fillet steak or vegetarians to a nut roast.
As the hours or days go by and the wind keeps them grounded their bellies empty and rampant hunger kicks in, driving their dreams of gorging themselves on human epidermis to frenzied heights.
When midges are in this mode if you listen very carefully when you are out and about in the highlands you can actually hear the sound of gnashing teeth in the grasses and heathers around you.
But we were fully experienced in these matters (oh, yes?) and using our not inconsiderable knowledge of nature considered there was no way the strong breeze could drop, so we decided to make the walk.
Down along a twisty path we went in our chest waders and after a while it turned out that the pool was actually further downstream than we had thought, but finally we arrived at it and began fishing.
And then some kind person turned the wind off.
Massive clouds of Scotland's secret weapon promptly took off from thousands of camouflaged airstrips, hurling themselves into the air virtually blotting out the sun. There were a minimum of one trillion, billion, quadrillion, gazillion of them dive bombing us.......and I am not exaggerating!
Well, maybe by just one or two.
We ran for it, but it made little difference, I could feel the growing lumps on my forehead as I ran as fast as my chest waders would allow. Everywhere relentless clouds of midges were making a midgeline straight for me. The sweat poured from me as I swatted at everything I could with my free hand, desperately trying to stop the biting until finally I reached my car, threw my rod in the heather and jumped in, along with a swarm of kamikaze midges that had sworn to eat or die.
I started the engine and put the fan on full blast, which sorted the blighters out a bit, and gradually I began to recover. I looked in the mirror at the great swollen, itching, blotches all over my face, neck and hands and mopped the last of the

sweat from my brow and there Alan and I sat in our cars, two supposed 'experts', surrounded and corralled by Scotland's secret weapon.
And then the same kind person turned the wind back on......

70. Winter Fishing

There was ice at the edges of the river and pieces of it, covered with snow, were floating downstream.
The temperature was just on freezing, but the stiff easterly breeze was taking the wind chill factor well below that point.
Before long the rod rings or the reels would begin freezing up.
There was a man fishing up above me and he did better than me that day.
We were worm fishing and I was having great difficulty as every time I got a worm out of my tin to put on the hook it froze solid and broke into pieces.
The man above me caught a nice fish just to cheer me up.
How was I going to fish? I had been told to bring worms and fish them and that was all I had. I looked upstream to see the man thumb his lip, as you might do before turning the page of a newspaper, and begin baiting up another hook. Was he using worms? If so how the hell was he managing?
He caught another fish as my hook again came back with nothing on it. There had been nothing on it after I had cast, the frozen fragment of worm I had managed to get to stick on had gone flying off before ever entering the water.
I looked up at the man as again he thumbed his lip and began baiting up again.
I was sure he was worming, so how was he doing it?
I went up and spoke with him, but he just mumbled at me. I couldn't understand him. I asked if he was worming. He pursed his lips and mumbled something unintelligible. I was becoming exasperated and the bitter cold wasn't helping, so I asked him why he just couldn't open his mouth and talk to me properly.
He pursed his lips and mumbled,
"It helps to keep the worms warm."

71. Jim and the Horsey Women

Jim Duncan was a good friend who worked for the Game Conservancy, utilising his considerable knowledge of game and game habitat. He was a great guy who loved fishing and shooting and we got on extremely well.
In July 1973 he invited me to fish the river Lochy, a good fly river, and I accepted as I loved to fish new water and learn new rivers.
I have no idea what possessed me to do it, but I threw a small spinning rod into the boot of my car and hid it under some clothing.
I stayed with Jim at his mother's house overnight and he told me to get down to the river quickly after breakfast the following morning and he would be along shortly. Arriving at the fishing hut I ran into three very 'horsey', hale and hearty type women, who would also be fishing that day. I cannot remember who they were but let's call them Dorothy, Hermione and Cynthia.
They asked where I had come from and when I said 'the Tay' they looked down their noses at me disapprovingly. Quite obviously the Tay, where people fished nasty things like shrimps and prawns at that time, was frowned upon by the three of them.
The Lochy was extremely high, running off a good flood and it had a brown tinge to it. I listened to the three of them discussing which flies they were going to use and Cynthia announced she was going to fish her 'Haiwy Maiwy' (Hairy Mary) on a floating line.
'Well, Cynthia, old girl,' I thought to myself, looking at the river as I put up my fly rod, 'if you catch anything with your Haiwy Maiwy out there today I'll eat my hat, my trousers, my car and this fishing hut'.
Their talk was all of country stuff, horses, fetes and fishing as Jim turned up and gave me a slightly embarrassed look after he had listened to their conversation for a minute, though it made little difference to me who I fished with and I didn't mind the three horsey women at all. In fact they were quite an act and their endless prattling served only to make me smile.
The old ghillie turned up and wished us all a 'good morning' in turn and then asked,
"Has anyone got a spinning rod with them?"
"A spinning rod?" asked Hermione as if someone had died.
Even the thought of a spinning rod seemed something far too distasteful for the three ladies to contemplate.
"Aye, a spinning rod."
I thought Cynthia might collapse at the mention of this heinously dreadful method of fishing, so I didn't jump in straight away.
"It's a spinning rod we need today ladies."
I cleared my throat and the old ghillie looked at me, knowing full well I had come from the Tay.
"Er,....I've got a ....er....ahem....one of those...um...things."
"Good!" he exclaimed. "Put it up quickly Mr.Miller, there's no time to lose!"
The three ladies were looking at me in shock, horror and complete disbelief, as if I was some kind of alien being as I took out my spinning rod and set it up. There was a lot of whispering going on between them and they kept looking in my

direction. Suddenly they walked off to go down to the lower part of the beat, apparently as far away from me as they could get in order not to witness the despicable act I was about to commit on their river.
Jim only had a fly rod, so he had a hard day ahead as the old ghillie and I took off to a place he knew where there was bound to be a fish.
He told me the fish would definitely be in and that my brown and gold weighted Devon was just the thing to be using. He put me on a small island of grass, just out from the bank, and had me cast to a specific ripple. Bang! A fish came on second cast and shortly I landed a beautiful sea liced ten pounder.
"Cast again," he urged and within fifteen minutes I had another one.
He had a satisfied look on his face when he said,
"Come on, Mr.Miller, there are other places we need to visit."
So off we went. He knew precisely where the fish would be, but if I didn't get a take within ten or fifteen minutes of fishing each new place we moved on.
At lunch I had three, all of them spanking fish straight from the sea and I had lost two. The horsey women, not having had a 'pull' from a fish between them, were quite disgusted and now totally disapproved of my presence.
In the afternoon I landed another three and lost four more.
Amongst the ones I got was a magnificent seventeen pounder, a bar of silver smothered with sea lice with long white tails. Towards the end of the day the old ghillie and I agreed the fish were now beginning to run hard and that we had seen the best of it.
The fly would most probably come in the following week as the river cleaned and fell and came into more suitable condition.
No one else had any fish, not even Jim unfortunately and the three horsey women looked upon my catch with brief, condescending admiration.....and then vanished.
Jim's mother was delighted with the fish and he asked if he could borrow my spinning rod to use the next day. He had never used an Ambassadeur so in their garden I showed him everything he would have to do and we made sure it was set so that it wouldn't overrun when he cast.
The following morning, as he headed for the Lochy, I headed south back to Dunkeld.
A couple of weeks later a member of our hotel staff told me someone had left a fishing rod at the back door of the hotel kitchens for me and there was my spinning rod with a note attached to it that read:
'Jim Duncan 3 - Horsey women 0'.

Loch Damph

72. Ferox!

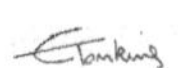

I had completely stopped fishing after 1996 when my life took some fairly disastrous turns. Now living quietly on the South African Cape the last thing on my

mind was that lurking somewhere deep in a Scottish loch was a monster Ferox brown trout and that one day we would meet in a fairly extraordinary fishing experience.
On arriving back in the UK at the beginning of 2002 I was contacted by an old friend and informed that an annual trout fishing competition was starting on his substantial highland loch in memory of Jim Duncan, our great friend and Game Conservancy worker, who died in the 1980's.
At that time I no longer had any fishable tackle or waders or even fishing clothing and had to borrow everything. Prepared as best I could I set off from London only to have my old car irreparably break down at Stoke on Trent, despite the sterling efforts of the Automobile Association. The potential nightmare of not getting to the highlands could only be averted by hiring a car and I transferred the wet and dry provisions I was transporting for the fishing party along with my gear to the new vehicle and set off once again.
The overnight stop with my friends Chris and Fiona in Edinburgh was most welcome, especially as Fiona is a cordon bleu chef, and early the next morning I drove up past my old fishing grounds along the river Tay and on to Inverness and beyond.
It was a bright, sunny Sunday but I was completely taken aback when suddenly I came upon the sight of nothing but darkness in the westerly direction I was now heading. Stopping the car I put on my loaned waterproof gear (I'm too long in the tooth to wait and see whether I'm going to get a soaking first) and a couple of miles down the road the deluge of rain was so forceful I had to stop the car until it abated and I could see out of the windscreen again.
I finally reached my destination in torrential rain whipped by strong winds, unpacked the car and settled down beside a welcome fire. That night the wind roared and the rain lashed against the windows, dashing all hopes of perfect trout fishing weather and by the next morning, Monday April 22nd, things were no better.
Still we all had a job to do in memory of Jim (who I swear I could hear chuckling quietly at us on the wind) and so being big, strong rufty-tufty mountain type people (well not really) we went trout fishing against all odds and all elements. By 11 o'clock even the hardiest of us were finding it tough going so we repaired to a nearby cottage, lit a fire, broke out the whisky and regaled each other with sporting stories from years gone by as the rain hammered down.
I was watching the squalls tearing wildly across the loch and the silvery fingers of streams running down the mountain face opposite, where normally there were no streams at all, when I informed the gathering it was my humble opinion that this considerable volume of fresh water would stir every fish in the loch and make them move, especially the big ones.
A few people threw things at me, but the general consensus was that 'as Miller doesn't know anything about fishing' the gathering shouldn't take a blind bit of notice. Such is the barracking that comes from old friendships. At a quarter to six in the evening Paul Zissler and Johnny Cooke-Hurle said they would pick me up on their way back to our lodgings in a half hour and I determined to fish along a promising shoreline.

Losing my dropper fly to the highland heather behind me (will I ever learn to cast properly?) I clambered up onto what has now been dubbed 'Miller's Rock', bit the dropper off, re-joined the cast and, with one lonely size 10 Connemara Black on the end of 5lb. breaking strain now joined Drennan leader, I zinged a perfect cast (for a change) a long way out into the loch and let it sink. The rain had stopped and the wind had backed off, so there were no more white horses chasing each other along on the tops of standing waves, the sky had lifted and there was just a blink of sun. It was five minutes to six.

I was thinking that this would have been the precise moment I would have been expecting something to hit me if I were fishing the Tay for salmon as, with the rod pointing down at the water below me, I very slowly stripped in the line.

Far too many years of fishing experience kicked in as the strength of the take pulled the rod up to the horizontal. Line began to peel off the reel and I thought 'now that's a really good take'. On and on went the fish in a long, steady, straight run as I looked with concern at the fast reducing amount of line I had left. Jumping straight into the loch from the rock I waded out as far as I could, holding the single handed fly rod as high as possible to keep the maximum amount of line out of the water and looked with trepidation at the few turns of backing left on the spindle. Just then the fish slowly drifted to a halt.

It was now some 75 yards away from me (I hasten to add that the next day I put 150 yards of backing on the loaned reel!).

For a second or two it seemed to be deciding whether to go on or not and then it gradually turned and ever so slowly came back towards me.

As I got it to within a dozen feet or so a car horn sounded and rude shouts came from behind as Paul and Johnny arrived. I shall not repeat the things they shouted at me for the sake of etiquette, but I could not turn or speak to them for even though I still had not seen the fish I was on autopilot, looking after its every move, watching for what I must do, anticipating. Then it took off on yet another run, equally as long as the first. This time it started off along the bank side to my right and then out in a gentle curve into the loch. Once again I held the rod as high as I could, lest the fish should break the 5lb. leader against the curve of the fly line under the water, and once again those last few turns of backing on the spindle were reached and once again, at the last possible moment, the fish came to a stop and turned back. Such is fortune.

I never saw it until it came to the net after 23 minutes of really hard going.

I managed to get it coming well, no shaking or thrashing about, and netted it first go. It was a big fish. My two friends were as stunned as I was.

As it lay there in the grass three lifetime's of fishing experience looked down at it and said the same thing,

'What on earth is it?".

That night the locals turned up to see it and we ran out of a week's supply of alcohol. The general consensus was that it was a Ferox because the scale count showed it to be trout family. Or was it something else? Some sort of landlocked sea trout perhaps? After all it only had three or four spots on its sides, so had Jess Miller at last discovered some new species? Would he go down in the annals of angling history in the same way the great explorers of our planet had upon making

such discoveries in the past? It is amazing how alcohol increasingly lets the imagination wander and also clouds the judgement.
We had no weighing scales for a fish of that size, so at 10.30 the following morning it was weighed on a brand new set of Salter scales and made exactly 15lbs.8ozs.
My host accused me of nothing less than ruining his competition on the very first day and my friends looked at me from time to time during the week and simply shook their heads. I was presented with the most wonderful trophy of a cold cast bronze trout leaping from a piece of drift wood and I have placed this adventure in the top five of my life's fishing experiences.

In a conversation some time later with angling friends at a trout fishery where all the fish are reared and stocked into the fishery every day someone mentioned my fifteen and half pounder. An old boy who was standing there looked dumbfounded and asked me,
"Was it wild?"
"Wild?" I replied, "it was bloody furious!"

A professional reading of the fish's scales showed it to indeed be a Ferox brown trout of some 16 years of age that had achieved great growth in its first six years and steady growth every year thereafter.
I presented a fibreglass cast replica of the fish to my host at the Jim Duncan Trophy in April the following year and readied myself to present the trophy to the next lucky recipient. Except for one tiny little problem.

On the same day in 2003, the 22nd April, competing for the Jim Duncan trophy once again and fishing with Paul Zissler from a boat this time, I hooked and landed a Ferox brown trout of 8lbs.10ozs. right next to the bank as we drifted into it, which gave me another twenty minute battle I would have lost had Paul Zissler not been handling the boat.

I was subsequently handicapped by four pounds in weight for the 2004 competition. Not only that but was told I would only be allowed to fish at night.........and without a rod!

In the event I fished for three of the six days and a friend won the competition with a trout of 3lbs.10ozs.

So I asked him if I could use it for bait!

73. Iced Lollies *(Popsicles in the USA!)*

At this Loch Damph fishing competition in 2006 Duncan, the owner, told me to ghillie Mike Clark and Steven Wade on the opening morning.
So they arrived halfway along the loch at the little cottage I was staying in, but it was a rough looking day.
I could see white horses crashing down the middle of the loch out from the point that sheltered the cottage and there had been a couple of pretty strong hail storms early in the morning.
One of them turned up in what appeared to be a new Range Rover with the number plate beginning with SAS, so I assumed, wrongly, he would be a hardy man.
He was wearing a tweed jacket and I warned both of them that when we got round the point and went up to where I wanted to take them we would be in the teeth of the wind and it would be extremely cold so they should kit themselves up appropriately.
We set off and everything I had said proved to be true.
We got up to a big rock where I wanted to begin our first drift and I turned the boat across the wind, shut off the engine and went to deploy the drogue. As I did so I took note of the darkness in the distance up the loch, when suddenly there was a shout and I heard a splash behind me.
SAS man had thrown his flies out there and a good trout had grabbed one!
I told them I didn't want to take the drogue in now that it was gripping and slowing our otherwise hectic speed of drift in the strong wind just as the trout shot under the boat. Steven Wade did very well with it and fortunately it didn't foul itself up with the drogue and came back out from under the boat on our side.
It began to hail, pinging off our backs as the wind really got up as the dark storm came over us.
The fight continued for several minutes before I netted the 6½ pounder that would win that year's competition and held my hand out to congratulate him.
They were both blue with cold!
I pulled in the drogue and raced flat out back to the cottage, got them in by the fire, threw some more wood and coal on it and we stayed there for some considerable time until the pair of iced lollies thawed out.

74. The Bait Ball

My pal Roger Still and I got special dispensation from Duncan to troll lures on Loch Damph, which is a fly only loch, and we saw some interesting things on our fish finder, especially large shoals of what looked like Char, good feeding for large trout.
One evening as we trolled along not far from the shore Roger exclaimed at something the fish finder was showing. Slowly we turned and came back over the area, and there it was again. We continued for a bit, turned and came back over it from a different angle.
It was a ball of bait fish!
Common in the sea when predators spook or drive bait fish into a ball so they can dive into them when feeding I had never heard of this happening in fresh water (but why wouldn't it?) and I said to Roger there must surely be some ferox close by to make the small fish do this.
We trolled up and down for half an hour and, one by one, the fish finder showed us three large fish lying off the bait ball.
Unfortunately 'large' on our fish finder meant 3 pounds or over so we couldn't tell what size they really were, but when one of them grabbed hold of one of our lures it proved to be around 7 pounds.
We slipped it back in and wondered at this experience.
We had done the same that I would have on the sea when finding a bait ball, troll up and down, covering the area all around it looking for the big predator that would out there.

75. Ethereal Light

I once trolled for trout on Torridon's Loch Damph with Roger Still from Bury St.Edmunds.
Torridon is a very special west coast Scottish location set amongst powerful scenery. Big mountains rise from sea or loch, golden eagles soar, red stags roar in the autumn and the midges bite the living daylights out of you between June and October.
Loch Damph can produce excellent wild brown trout and we fished in April, a good time of the year with the wild brownies coming onto spring feeding after their sparsely nourished winter.
The weather was diabolical.
Great lashing rainstorms tinged with hail hammered at us, the temperature was well down and the light was dismally low. It wasn't too pleasant being out there at the mercy of the elements. The day grew darker and darker in mid-afternoon, as if night was coming on early. It was the eeriest kind of dingy light that we fished in and, unsurprisingly, we were fishless.
Trolling down the centre of the loch in the murkiness a sudden searchlight shaft of light appeared direct from the heavens and began to move across the mountainside opposite us. A thin, concentrated shaft that was so bright we remarked upon its extraordinary brilliance and presence on such a dark day.

Mesmerised by it we watched as it began to cross from the mountain slowly onto the loch. It was quite something.
All around us was dark and here was a veritable pillar of pure white light moving slowly and silently along.........and it was coming straight at us.
We weren't convinced that it would actually come upon us as we trolled on, but a few minutes later it did just that, blinding us with its powerful light so that we were forced to shield our eyes and we both exclaimed loudly at the overwhelming brilliance of it as we were bathed in searing white light.
Then it moved away, travelling ever so slowly on its way across the water.
It got some fifty yards from us when in an instant it went out, just as if someone had thrown a switch, and we were left to fish our extremely murky day remarking upon the extraordinary ethereal light that had shined upon us.

On The Piddle

76. The John Wayne Epic!

Another memorable time I hooked myself was in the 1970's when fishing the river Piddle in Dorset, a highly underestimated salmon river on which I was fishing a large Mepps spoon, casting it upstream and reeling it back down the river at speed. Salmon would come shooting out from under the banks of this marvellous little river, no more than ten yards wide, and nail the Mepps as it came flying down the middle.

They were good fish too. I caught a couple just over 20 pounds and a 28 and a 32 pounder were caught during the years I fished it.

Before World War II two fish of over 40 pounds had been caught on that beat, I believe both on the same day, but stand to be corrected.

Using all my sharply honed fishing skill with great accomplishment I successfully hooked a bush on the opposite bank. I found the Mepps was clinging on to it for dear life. So I very stupidly (using all the vast resources from my lifetime's fishing experience) made sure I was directly opposite it, grabbed the line and began to pull at the resisting bush harder and harder. The bush came towards me out over the river until the point of no return was reached with the line virtually on breaking point.

Suddenly there was a loud 'Spang'!

The Mepps left the bush at the speed of light, crossed the river in a flash a kingfisher would have been proud of and embedded itself firmly into my forearm.
I took one look at it, with the shaft of the treble hooks lying tight along my skin, realised it wasn't going to come out of there very easily, cut the line with my teeth and began to walk back to the fishing hut.
Duncan Gray was fishing with me that day so I showed him my predicament.
He informed me in utter delight that he just happened to have a brand new razor blade with him… as well as a bottle of whisky.
Visions of the old John Wayne movie, where I think it was Ward Bond's poisoned thumb that had to be cut off and they distracted his attention from the coming severing by regaling him with stories and encouraging him to drink most of a bottle of whisky flashed through my mind.
So I took a massive slug of neat whisky and then another that started my eyes watering.
My forearm was now aching as Duncan held the shaft of the treble hook and pulled it gently away from the skin. The barb of the hook deep underneath made a lump and Dunc looked at me, again in delirious happiness, and suggested I should take some more whisky, quite a lot of whisky in fact.
I duly obliged. Well, who was I to argue?
Then, pulling the hook up again he quickly slit the skin with the razor blade and pulled the hook straight out. He did it so well it was a bit of an anti-climax really, to make up for which he then poured neat whisky into the wound and my eyes began to water again.
Before joining me in a dram he said,
"It was worth driving from the other side of the country just for the pleasure of doing that!"
So I finally found out what our fishing buddies are for.....

Tales of Jake

Jake, also known as Big Jake, Shakey Jake, Shakery Jakery and Buggalugs, was my big black Labrador gun dog and we were a team from 1970 when he entered the world up at Calvine, above Blair Atholl, until he passed away in 1984.
We had many wonderful and hilarious adventures together so here are a few of the fishing ones:

77. Take A Dive

I used to take a walk down to the Gage Tree pool at Dunkeld House in the early mornings and fish it through as long as hotel guests were not intending to do so. Many guests would not start fishing until 9.30am or later and would miss those early morning fish that had stopped for the night, but which would take off to run the river hard again once the light was up or once they felt the morning rise in water from the hydro dam at Pitlochry.
Jake and I would saunter down the riverbank to wait for the light and I would be dressed in normal day clothes as I could tail a fish out by hand in the Gage and didn't need waders.
One morning we were down there and a couple of fish had shown themselves.
I was throwing a metal Devon across the river on a long line, landing it well over onto the Fifey bank, mending my line, reeling it slowly to make sure it didn't stick over there on the shallow bank and then leaving it to swim slowly across the middle of the river.
I was fishing from the left hand bank and turned to take a step downstream, right leg across left, when a fish hit the Devon so hard out in the middle that it pulled me straight off the top of the bank into the river!
I threw the rod upstream before hitting the water, barked my shins on the bottom and surfaced to grab the rod again and found the fish had gone.
I reeled the Devon in, clipped it to the reel and turned to get out of the water and there was Big Jake standing above me giving me one of his looks.
He was a dog whose looks said everything and spoke volumes about any situation and this particular look was saying a few things, such as:
'Er, correct me if I'm wrong, but aren't I the one whose supposed to jump in the river?'
Or 'Ah, invented a new game have we? How does this one go then?'
Or 'Who's a clever boy, then?'

78. A Face Full of Salmon

On the 8th March 1973 Jake and I were up at the Rock Pool with the river running at a big height and perfect for spring fish to be moving on through.
Again I was fishing a Devon on a long line, throwing it over to the Rock on the other bank from high up above on the bend, mending my line and letting it swim slowly through the pool.
Before long I got a strong take and hooked a fish that stayed where it was for some minutes and then began to swim upstream, coming right up opposite me, but then continuing on up into the Ivy Tree pool on the far bank, above a big backwater that lies above the Rock.
I had filled my reel with brand new 18lb. line the night before and so I put the fish under serious pressure as it got to the head of the Ivy Tree up above me and it turned and came back down the middle of the river at speed to end up where I had hooked it. Then it began moving upstream again. A fish has to have weight to be able to do this kind of thing so I knew it was a good one.
When it got up into the Ivy the second time I managed to turn it again and bring it much closer to my bank as it came down the river straight towards me.
Standing high on the bend in the strong sunlight I could see it clearly as it slowly came past in the quieter water heading for the strong stream below and I could see every scale on it. I gave it all the pressure I could and watched as it took not a blind bit of notice and carried on straight past me with its big tail wafting back and forth.
It was now only three yards from the shingle on my bank, but it wasn't stopping and there came a point where I realised that it wasn't going to turn, but was going to leave the Rock Pool and go down into the Ferry and it would be quite a job for me to follow it. In that second I had to make a decision and decided to go after it and gaff it to reduce the odds of losing it down in the Ferry.
So I unclipped my gaff and extended it, holding it along with the rod in my left hand as I began to run and wind in the line as fast as I could. Jake, being a young dog at that time, thought this was great fun and ran alongside me, but the spit of gravel we were on was quickly running out so, as I got opposite the fish, I ran into the water and stuck the gaff in it, lifted it out and hurled it through the air onto the bank, where it hit Jake squarely in the face!
He screamed and took off like a black bolt of lightning and disappeared over the top of the bank.
I knocked the fish on the head. It was a beautiful 28 pounder. I washed it off and sorted myself out, looked round and there was this little black face with a paw to either side of it looking at me cautiously over the top of the bank.
This time the look said:
'What did I do wrong?'
Or, 'If this is your idea of a new game I don't want to play it.'
Or, 'Any more flying salmon about or is it safe to come out now?'

79. Fishing Games

When he was very young I would train Jake by letting him carry my hat, then bring it to me and I'd give it back so he could carry it again.
Thus he gained an affinity for hats.
Being the brains of the outfit he quickly worked out that when I came out of the river and sat on the bank doing things with my hands, like undoing a fankle or unravelling a birds nest of line on my Ambassadeur or tying on a new bait or fly cast, I was fair game as I was busy and couldn't get at him. So he would invariably sneak up and pull my hat off and run away with it. As he got older he would pull it off and sit only just out of reach of me with his big rudder of a tail slapping the ground, knowing full well what he had managed to get away with.
Sometimes though I got a bit wily myself and pretended to be doing something with my hands whilst watching him out of the corner of my eye, then I would make a grab for him when he sneaked in to get my hat and we had many a rough and tumble on the river bank with Jake making mock attacks and me pretending to give in, then attacking him again.
If anyone had seen us they would have thought us completely mad.
Another thing he would do on the odd occasion when I was busy with my hands would be to sit next to me fully upright, sniffing the wind as usual, then jab me in the ear with his big, wet, cold nose.
Charming.

80. The Flying Dog Cure - *Taken from my self help book 'We're All In This Together', helping you get through stressful and depressing times in your life.*

Once we had to get up to the Orkney Isles in a hurry on a sudden invitation to go duck shooting, but the ferries out of Scrabster on the North East coast of Scotland were on strike and the only way was to fly, however the scheduled flights were full. So I hired a small aircraft from a new private air service called Peregrine and Jake and I turned up with all our gear at Edinburgh airport ready to go. Everything was fine until our pilot saw Jake. He was terrified of him. He kept walking around me saying he refused to take the dog, making sure to keep me between him and Jake all the time. He'd had problems with dogs in the air before and, to be fair, if you have a problem up there in a small aircraft you certainly don't want one with teeth at one end of it.
But Jake was as easygoing as he was harmless and never hurt anyone in his life. I could put other dogs in his kennel with him and little kids used to love to pet him with Jake never giving any kind of a problem.
So I took my time and over about half an hour managed to persuade the terrified pilot to fly us up to Kirkwall in the Orkneys.
It was blowing a gale as we walked out to the aircraft and he asked me to get the dog up into the four seater cockpit. I told Jake to jump up on the wing, which he did, then to jump into the cockpit, which he did, then to jump over into the back seats, which he did and sat there looking at us. The pilot looked at me in astonishment and I told him not to give Jake a second thought as we stowed the last of our gear and climbed in.
He warned me that it would be a rough ride up to 3,000 feet and then it would be quiet. Having flown all my life I told him it wasn't a problem.
We took off and the plane bounced about a lot. I remember looking back at Jake who was sitting looking out of the window, swaying around completely unconcerned as if he did this every day. Eventually we hit 3,000 feet and it was plain sailing from then on. After a while the pilot took his headphones off and turned to say something to me.
Jake promptly took his pilot's peaked hat off and sat there holding it, wagging his tail as if to say: 'By the way, did you know I can do this?'
The pilot jumped in alarm so I smiled at him, asked Jake to give me the hat back and took it as the big Lab offered it to me. Now the pilot was even more astonished. He put his hat back on, turned to speak to me once more and Jake promptly took his hat off again. This time I told the pilot just to ask Jake for it and he would give it back to him and I watched the terrified man take his hat back as Jake released it ever so gently.
By the time we landed at Kirkwall I could not separate the two of them.
Not only was the pilot completely over his fear he was giving Jake his peaked cap and taking it back at will, petting the big dog and playing with him.
Jake had completely cured him.
For his part Jake was playing along with the pilot and kept giving me looks that said:
'Look at me, I've cured him! Look, he's eating out of my hand!'

My friends were waiting for us to get going, but still I couldn't part Jake and the pilot until I gave Jake a sharp command and a look that said:
'OK smartarse, if you want any food tonight you better come now!'
Then he came at a run.

81. Life Change

It was Joe Eliot who spotted that Jake would go blind as we stood in the bar at Dunkeld House one day with the sun streaming in through the windows and across Jake's eyes. Sure enough we found out Jake's mother had gone blind and I had not been told.
So between the ages of nine and ten my great friend lost his sight.
I thought that would be the end of it and had a hard time reconciling the fact that this great dog, who used to sit crouched opposite me when flighting pigeons as I watched his eyes that signalled when birds were coming in from behind me and from which side so keen was his eyesight, would now only be half the dog he had been.
I couldn't have been more wrong.
Jake adjusted to his blindness perhaps as only an animal can and accompanied me to the fishing every day I was out as well as to the shooting, especially if we were on open ground.
His sense of smell was so keen that a phenomenon arose at the hotel with guests who asked if they could take him for a walk.
How many would come back and ask if I was sure he was blind.
They had headed off to go on a certain walk, but Jake often had different ideas of where to go and had taken them all over the hotel grounds, down paths they never knew existed, and had never put a foot wrong.

He lived a full, happy and adventurous life, was the greatest gun dog I could ever have wished for and lived to the age of thirteen and a half years.

Tales of the Brigadier

82. Cast of a Lifetime

Brigadier Lindsay Valentine Francis Fawkes was the all time quintessential English gentleman. Nicknamed 'Guy' during his army days he stood tall and erect and spoke perfect Queen's English. He was an honest and pleasant man with whom I spent many hours talking about everything to do with fishing down through the years he fished with us at Dunkeld House Hotel.

Unfortunately the Brig was not that good a fisher from the river bank, although he became better in time.

He came to us once or twice every year for many years without catching a fish whilst fishing from the bank, although he did catch quite a number from the boat and certainly knew how to handle them.

He fished heavy braided line on a red Ambassadeur multiplier and one year I noticed he was putting a massive effort into his casting, but his lure was travelling barely 15 yards out across the water. When we were back in the fishing room I asked him about it and found I could hardly get his reel to run free. When I offered to service it, the Brig looked perturbed, never having heard of anyone 'stripping and servicing' a fishing reel before.

I told him not to worry and settled down back in my cottage to sort the reel out, but when I opened it up I found it to be full of a hard, congealed black substance that covered every moving part. It had probably never seen oil from day one and the original grease or whatever someone had put in it at sometime had seemingly 'baked' itself onto everything. I could only get it off by the continuous scraping of all of the internal parts with a knife.

It was the longest time I have ever taken to service a multiplier, but in the end I got it back to almost new condition and lubricated properly with the clutch purring away smoothly. I gave it back to the Brig the next morning, making sure he knew how to set it and warned him that it would now really go, so not to put too much effort into his casting.

I was in the boat with Jimmy McLean when the Brig arrived down below the hotel and we watched as he cast from the high bank and his spoon sailed a way out across the river, landing not that far off the other bank, some 60 to 70 yards distant.

The Brig got such a shock he only just stopped himself falling from his high perch into the river! Then he looked across at us in sheer astonishment at having cast further than he ever had before!

83. The Great Wader

The Brig was a ferocious wader and I really mean ferocious.
I waded the Tay most of my life and have nothing but the utmost respect for the powerful currents of this great river, but Brigadier Guy Fawkes simply attacked it, boldly wading where no man had gone before, most probably.
I watched him on many occasions struggling to cross strong currents (the Tay runs at around 8 knots) to get to his objective, usually a place where the last fish had been caught during the year nineteen oat cake, but that didn't matter to the Brig, he was going to get there come hell or literally high water.
I tried to wade to some of these places, but even with my youth and strength found it a most unpleasant experience.
One day I watched him battle across the river just above the hotel and somehow, after the greatest of effort, make it over to the far bank, only to find he was in a place where he couldn't possibly fish because to one side of him there was heavy foliage overhanging fast water and to the other side a backwater.
He stayed there for a while, regaining his breath and strength, and then proceeded to fight his way back the way he had come. Why he did this I shall never know, but I admired his determination even though I was terrified we would lose him and, with the saying that there are old waders and bold waders, but there are no old, bold waders in mind, I told him so on more than one occasion.
He took absolutely no notice!

84. Bowling Along

One day I was out in the boat harling Green Point, a quiet, deep pool with Jimmy and David Morris when a bowler hat came floating quietly past us.
David looked at it and said,
"Amazing to think the Brigadier's riding along on a bicycle underneath that!"

85. Winning In The End

The miracle finally occurred on the 10th October 1972 when Brigadier Guy Fawkes caught a 21 pounder from the bank in the Kings Ford in front of the hotel. It had taken him four years of trying and to say he was elated is an understatement.
He was over the moon.
Beaming at us all with a satisfied grin on his face he bought drinks in the bar and was hailed as a hero because everyone in the hotel knew how desperate he had been to catch his first salmon from the river bank.
In the dining room Peggy, our head waitress, made a fuss of him and we presented him with a bottle of wine to enjoy with his meal.
It was the Brigadier's day.
I was looking at his magnificent fish in the sink in the fishing room when he appeared after dinner and he and I went over the story of how his success had

happened again. But when I asked him whether we should freeze or smoke it for him to take home, a look of utter horror came over his face.
“Take it home? Oh, no, I couldn’t possibly do that! My wife wouldn't hear of it! No, no I can’t take it home! Absolutely not!”
I felt sorry for this good and kindly man who had expended so much time, effort and money to catch a wonderful Tay salmon from the riverbank only to be faced with not being able to enjoy it with his family and friends.
Eventually though my brain engaged gear and we ensured that enjoy it with his friends he did.
Our chef prepared it for him and he shared it with the many hotel guests he knew so well.

86. Beating the System?

One day the Brig came to me and asked for a hacksaw.
Now I had never heard of anyone fishing for salmon with a hacksaw, but seeing that this was the Brig I duly found him one.
Many hours later he returned it to me with a satisfied look on his face and confided,
“Going home tomorrow, putting my car on the train. Got those buggers on the Motorail sorted now though. I measured my car by using an ingenious method of hanging weights off either end of it then marking it out with chalk on the ground in your car park. Did it three times to get it absolutely right and it was three quarters of an inch too long to qualify for the lower rate. So I cut those rubber bits off the front of the bumper and now it qualifies! Saved myself a bit of money there I can tell you.”
I didn’t have the heart to tell him that the rates were designated by the make and model of the car putting it in a certain size category and I have wondered ever since how he got on with his plan at Perth Motorail Depot.
He never mentioned it to me thereafter though.

I liked the Brigadier, he was one of the great characters that give fishing and life such enjoyable richness.

From the Daily Telegraph Obituaries:

Brigadier Guy Fawkes, who has died aged 90 (October 3rd 2003), was awarded an MC in an action in front of the Gazala Line, North Africa, in 1942 and a DSO in an attack on the Mareth Line the next year.

On April 9th 1942, Fawkes, then a major in command of a battery of 74 Field Regiment RA, was operating with a mixed column of tanks, artillery and infantry forward of the Gazala Line.
The column was heavily shelled and attacked by tanks, but he set a fine example by his coolness under fire at one of his troop positions.
When three guns had been put out of action and the entire detachment of the fourth had been killed or wounded, Fawkes continued to fire the remaining gun until all his ammunition was exhausted.
He was the last to leave and, after making sure that his other troop had withdrawn safely, he went back to try to recover the gun sights, although it was almost certain that the position was in enemy hands.
He was awarded an immediate MC (Military Cross).....

.....On the night of March 20 1943, Fawkes's battery had the task of providing fire support to the 8th Battalion Durham Light Infantry in the attack on the heavily-defended Mareth line.
When the battalion commander of the Durhams was killed and the second-in-command wounded, Fawkes encouraged the men to get forward while he crossed the Wadi Zigzaou under heavy machine-gun fire and dug himself an observation post which he occupied throughout the next day.
Fawkes sent back vital information, and when the battalion withdrew and his post came under tank fire, he continued to direct his battery on the advancing armour and infantry. His actions at a critical time were recognised by the award of the DSO (Distinguished Service Order).

Anecdotes

87. Who Needs Rods?

I once arrived at Redgorton with my party of fishers hot from Dunkeld House to be greeted by ghillies Sandy Penney and Alf Campbell. There was great crack going on and everyone was in good form. I was pulling on my waders when Sandy and Alf appeared from the back of my Land Rover and said,
"We know you're pretty good at this salmon fishing lark, Mr.Miller, but surely you need rods?"
I had forgotten them!

88. Anchors Aweigh!

On another occasion I ghillied David Morris for an afternoon on Upper Murthly because Jimmy MacDonald had a medical appointment to attend.
Having harled much of the beat we decided to anchor up and fish the Girnal, so I went to the bow and threw Jimmy's brand new anchor over the side.
Unfortunately it wasn't tied on to anything!
When we met Jimmy the next morning we were humming 'Anchors Aweigh'!

89. Cobblers!

My aunt Joan was once quizzing me in the bar at the hotel about the life of the salmon and all the different names it was called at various stages of its life.
She told me that a man had told her the pool below the Hermitage falls on the river Braan was absolutely stuffed with forty pound salmon.
"Cobblers aunty, " I replied.
My aunt seemed bemused and studied her drink for a while.
"Well," she said finally, "I still don't understand all these different terms you use. What's the difference between a Cobbler and a Kelt?"

90. Cock of the North!

One fisherman who came to fish with Jimmy McLean at the hotel used to have a curious pet. A Cockerel!
I remember its plumage as being dark with gold around its neck.
It had a ferocious look in its eye and could give you a nasty peck.
Jimmy was not keen on it at all and kept telling the gentleman that having it running around in the boat was a real nuisance what with the rods, tackle and hooks that were around.
But the man would have none of it.
One year though there came a day when a fish came on the middle rod and before the man could pick the rod up the cockerel had attacked the handle of the fly reel that was spinning round and round at a furious rate as the fish tore line from it and received a serious blow from the handle to its head as a result.
Unconscious it then got caught up in the line and became jammed in against the first ring on the rod where the pressure from the fish throttled it and there it expired.
The man was so distraught he asked Jimmy to dispose of it.
So Jimmy took it home, plucked it, cleaned it, roasted it and ate it!

91. A Bit of Perspective

A lawyer from London once walked to the top of Craigie Barns, the mountain behind Dunkeld House, with Jimmy McLean and I (we took the easy route). Once on top the views are stupendous. As we left to walk home Jimmy passed a dead branch hanging from a small tree.
The branch had a completely smooth, polished indentation worn in it where it had been rubbing against another branch.
"Hmm," said Jimmy, "been swinging in the wind."
Our lawyer looked at the piece of wood and I could feel the thoughts running through his mind.
'How long has this stick been here blowing back and forth rubbing against this tree to become worn so smooth, whilst I've been commuting back and forth to my office in London every day, breathing in foul air and working my guts out.'

Just the thought of it brought him up short as he suddenly realised there were simple things like this continuously going on in nature all the time he was buried in a somewhat limited world into which a bit of perspective had now crept.

92. A Seriously Big Fish

'Rhombo' Brown and his wife from Betws-y-Coed in Wales were once harling the Cathedral Stream with Jimmy in late autumn.
The river had settled back after a spate and was not that high, however the autumn fish were coming forward in numbers as night frosts dropped the water temperature and urged them on.
As they made a turn in at the Cathedral wall and proceeded back across the river a fish of simply staggering proportions rose immediately behind the boat. It came completely out of the water and Mr.Brown, who had landed many really big salmon, told me later that it was by far the biggest he had ever seen and Jimmy confirmed it had been pretty massive.
As the wave that came from the fish landing back in the water spread out across the river Mr.Brown leaned forward and said to Jimmy,
"Would you be so kind as to move the boat across and let that fish get past us, Mr.McLean!"

93. Spray Day

One reason we bought Dunkeld House was that I had been really seriously ill. Instead of becoming a sprinter with a chance of getting somewhere in my sport after I came out of school I had been rendered unable to walk, never mind sprint. The idea was for me to recuperate by working in the woods, fishing and sleeping wherever and whenever I needed to as my body tried to heal itself.
I had been told I would never sprint again (I ran 10.8 for 100 metres at the age of twenty seven though, just to prove the doctors wrong, however that was the same time I had been running at eighteen and the ability go faster had left me).
I went down to the boat after lunch one blustery afternoon to wait for Jimmy and, not feeling at all well, lay across the two seats that the anglers sat on and went to sleep. From time to time the strong wind would whip spray from the surface of the river and it would land on me. I was so exhausted I simply brushed it off my face each time. It went on and on, with more and more spray landing on me as the wind blew, on and on it went and.... wait a minute!
The wind hadn't been blowing when that last bit of spray landed on me!
I got up and there was McLean crouched by the bow of the boat, scooping water and throwing it up into the wind so that it was blowing all over me.
He was red in the face from stopping himself laughing and I was completely soaked!

94. Rock of Ages!

There was a frantic search on for me at the hotel one day as it seemed a gentleman had hooked a monster salmon up in the Rock Pool.
I grabbed my telescopic gaff and ran all the way up there to find him indeed attached to something big out in the river. It was high water and there was strong current travelling through this normally slightly lazy pool. He and his wife were in a highly excited state and he told me what had happened over the last fifty minutes that he had been fighting the fish.
I looked at his tackle and the line he was using and it all looked far too light to be fishing with in this height of water to me.
Then the clutch on the reel went as the fish took line, stopped and he wound down, tightened up on it and lifted the rod again.
As a surge of current boiled out in the middle the fish took line again and he repeated what he had just done.
The Rock Pool is so called because of the large rock on the opposite bank that shelves down into the water, but those of us who know the pool well also know that there is another rock, shaped a bit like the Matterhorn out in the middle of the river and fractionally below the one on the bank.
Perhaps it is this rock, that anglers have lost so much tackle on over the years, the pool should have been named after.
Our gentleman angler was firmly attached to the Matterhorn and disappointingly for him not to a fish at all.
With his tackle being so light the surging current was able to take line from his reel that he could get back once the surge was past, until the next surge came and he lost line again. It was quite a dilemma for me because although I told him that this was the case I could see that his desperation for what he had hooked to be a record salmon, so that he could take his place in angling history, was fuelling his disbelief.
I showed him the surging boil whenever it came and, lo and behold, he lost line that he quickly gained back afterwards every time.
It must have been almost half an hour before he finally accepted the fact that what he had on the end of his line was not a leviathan, but Bonny Scotland.

95. April Fools

One April our hotel guests came down to the fishing room in the morning to find it empty!
All of their rods, tackle, tackle bags, clothing and waders had gone!
They found the door from the tackle room into our back yard had not been locked.
Someone had stolen everything so we immediately called the police.
Everyone was interviewed.
Jimmy was eventually able to start fishing about 11.00a.m. and took the boat up the Rock Pool at the top of our beat, whilst the last hotel guests were still being interviewed, giving descriptions of everything they had lost.
As they approached the Rock Pool Jimmy spied something unusual on the river bank ahead of them though, which turned out to be a large pile of all the missing items!
It turned out to be April 1st!
Thankfully even the police saw the funny side of it.

96. Space Launch

When ABU replaced their red Ambassadeur with the black one I got hold of one of the first available, serviced and oiled it, loaded it with line and walked down to show it to Jimmy, who was just coming in with the boat.
The man who was fishing with him saw my black Ambassadeur and declared he didn't know why I bothered with it as they were useless for casting.
Whilst he went on making caustic comments, Jimmy asked if I thought it was any better than the red one.

I said there was only one way to find out and, standing on top of the high wall above them, I clicked the reel into free run, swung it back with my thumb on the drum and launched a one ounce Toby out across the river.
It landed high in the trees about seventy yards away on the opposite bank!
The man in the boat went quiet and looked glum whilst Jimmy looked at me and shook his head at the distance the lure had gone.
It's probably still up there in the trees.

97. Lost and Found

I ghillied for a couple of Bill Lowrie's friends one January day and we hooked a fish at the Grey Stone croy and I beached the boat on the right hand bank.
As the fish came in towards the boat it shook its head and the hook and the Kynoch Killer flew out of the river and up into a tree above us.
I plunged down with the net as I saw the fish turn down deep to make its way back out into the river and it swam straight into the net.
The two men were busy looking up into the tree to try and get the Kynoch down from it and hadn't a clue we had the fish. So I dispatched it and lay it in the boat between us. They did very well to get the Kynoch unhooked from the branches and were so apologetic about having lost a spring fish. They really were quite upset so I told them not to worry and think nothing more of it.
We set about harling Green Point and still they hadn't seen the fish, even though they had placed their rods in the rod holders, with the butts lodged back in the slots under their seats only several inches from it.
Eventually one of them said,
"I really wish we'd got that fish, Jess, it's a long time since I've seen a springer."
"Well, there's one lying right there." I said, pointing to the fish lying at my feet.
They were two extremely surprised and delighted anglers!

98. Unstoppable Salmon

Once at Oykel Bridge I looked over into the river Oykel in low water and saw two salmon lying there.
One seemed to be eighteen or nineteen pounds and the other ten or twelve pounds. I wondered how they were going to get up the river in such low water, but when I came back from breakfast in the nearby Oykel Bridge Hotel they had gone, showing how determined fish are to travel onwards and get up rivers in almost any conditions.

99. A Bit of Shakespeare

It is a well known Scottish custom that has to be said to bring luck when at the riverside before deciding which spoon to fish with:
'Toby or not Toby, that is the question.'
If you don't say this you won't catch a fish!

100. Help! Help!

Ghillie Sandy Penney had the ability to cry 'Help! Help!' in a tiny, high pitched voice without moving his lips.
He used to do it when running the boat back up the river and you could barely make it out above the noise from the outboard engine.
It could be quite disturbing if you didn't know Sandy was responsible for it.
One lady made him stop the boat and search up and down the river bank for half an hour to try and find whoever it was that had been crying out she was so perturbed by it.
Served him right!

More Stories to Come:

I am writing more books of fishing and shooting stories from the UK and around the world.

Please send me your fishing and shooting stories for inclusion in future books, just be sure to let me know whether they're true or false!
Please send them to me through www.TrueorFalseFishingStories.com

They should not only be stories about the amazing things that happened when you were actually fishing or shooting, but things that happened on the way there or on the way back, how your planning of a sporting holiday did or didn't work out, the triumphs, disasters, hilarity and strange occurrences surrounding your fishing and shooting experiences. The more humorous they are the better.

And don't forget to send fishing jokes and anecdotes for inclusion too!

Jess

Jess Miller helps people beat their life problems at: www.EnergyThieves.com
His self help books and audio books help people beat problems with: Alcohol, Drugs, Tobacco, Bullying, Stealing, Gambling, Gangs, Knives, Guns, Emotions, Food, People, Major Problems, Traumas, Stress, Depression, Idle Gossip, Bigotry, Hypocrisy, Self Importance, Narcissism, Arrogance, Judgementalism and most of the things that can so easily damage our lives.

EnergyThieves.com